A Letter From the Co-Founders of Sec

Dear Customer,
We're delighted that you've purchased a Secondary Entrance practice pack! Before you begin of Secondary Entrance, and what our ethos is when it comes to providing education services.

As of June 2017, we had both been privately tutoring students for multiple years, and at a c̶ ̶ ̶ ̶ ̶ ̶ ̶ conversation we realised that we shared a few common frustrations. Firstly, we felt that existing practice tests for 11+ students appeared to focus on coaching exam technique rather than training aptitude. Secondly, materials in the existing market seemed to be grossly overpriced, and money was increasingly becoming a factor in academics. We also both understand that it is only healthy for a child to work a limited number of hours in a day, and that it is therefore crucial to make the most out of every working minute. Lo and behold, Secondary Entrance was born.

We set a goal: to develop affordable new resources of the highest quality. Together, we recruited the best minds from top universities in the world to create training tests for the four main pillars of secondary school admission: maths, English, verbal reasoning and non-verbal reasoning. Every question has been hand-crafted, debated over and scrutinised to ensure that it meets our exceptionally high standards. We ensured that the papers liberally use graphics to help develop children's visual and spatial skills alongside their intellect. In total, we've produced resources that give your child every chance of gaining admission to the school of their choice.

While our papers educate as well as monitor, we know that there is no substitute to having a good teacher. As such, we decided to compile a portfolio of tutors to offer both in-person and online tuition. We personally interviewed a wide range of candidates, selected the very best and trained them to Secondary Entrance quality. To complete our offerings, we've also uploaded a range of free resources on www.Independent11Plus.co.uk that we're constantly building on. Whatever it is that you need, we want to make sure that we've got you and your child covered. We'd like to wish your child all the best in their academic endeavours, not only for their upcoming exams but also for the journey that follows.

Warmest regards and happy testing,

Founders of Secondary Entrance
www.SecondaryEntrance.co.uk

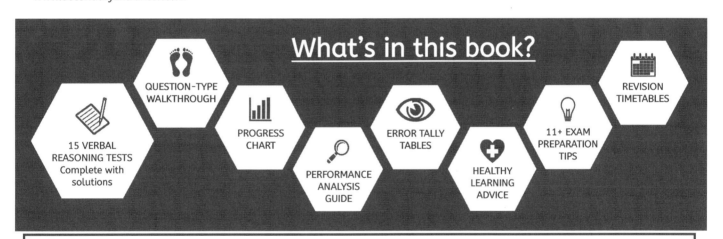

What's in this book?

- QUESTION-TYPE WALKTHROUGH
- REVISION TIMETABLES
- 15 VERBAL REASONING TESTS Complete with solutions
- PROGRESS CHART
- PERFORMANCE ANALYSIS GUIDE
- ERROR TALLY TABLES
- HEALTHY LEARNING ADVICE
- 11+ EXAM PREPARATION TIPS

What makes these books so special?

There are three core aspects to what makes our papers unique, and which allow us to best support your child:

Quality
We offer the highest quality 11+ practice papers on the market, suitable for independent schools.

Diversity
We have 240 varied 11+ papers across four subjects, and our content is highly enriched with graphics and visuals.

Flexibility
Our papers get harder from Book 1 to 4 in each subject, and are all also highly effective for general aptitude training.

11+ Practice Papers
For Independent Schools & Aptitude Training

Verbal Reasoning

Book 1

Orders: Please contact www.How2Become.com

ISBN: 9781912370740

First published in 2020 by How2Become Ltd.

As part of this resource, you are entitled to claim a 30-day free trial to our powerful online Independent 11+ Online Tuition Course...

GET FREE ACCESS NOW:

www.My11PlusCourse.co.uk

- ☑ 30+ Video Tuition Modules on Maths, English, Verbal Reasoning, and Non-Verbal Reasoning;
- ☑ 100s of interactive practice questions;
- ☑ Detailed answers to each question – ensure you can help your child learn how to pass each question type;
- ☑ Over 6 Hours of Tuition for Your Child;
- ☑ The only Independent School 11+ online tuition, practice, & mock-exam resource – from How2Become and Secondary Entrance;
- ☑ Try free for 30 days!

Contents

Verbal Reasoning - Walkthrough

Sample test, ordered by question type, with worked solutions and tips

Instructions for Usage:

> Run through this guide before attempting any of the papers.
> Attempt all of the questions, then review the worked solutions given.
> After completing tests, use this syllabus guide to find out weak topics.
> You can best document weak topics in the error tally table.

1) REMOVING SUBSET WORDS

Sample Question: 3 consecutive letters have been taken out of a word. Select which three letter word has been omitted, from the options. Write your answer below:

The W___HOUSE was packed with so many boxes!

A. LIP   B. BID   C. ARE   D. BAR   E. ONE

Answer and Explanation: C, ARE. This type of question assesses your child's ability to understand the context of a sentence, and the spelling of particular words too. There are two ways to answer this question, based on the assessment of these two parts of verbal reasoning. One could infer from the context of the sentence that W__HOUSE is warehouse, as this is where boxes could be stored. If this fails, and you are unable to solve the question, look at the 5 options you are presented with: WLIPHOUSE, WBIDHOUSE, WAREHOUSE, WBARHOUSE and WONEHOUSE. Even if you may never have heard of the word warehouse, the other options simply do not make sense as words. Therefore, an educated guess would be to choose warehouse.

Tips: Write out the 5 options to fill in the blank to get a view of the words. Sometimes the sentence will not be there to help you, and you may see the word just by itself, but if you are given context then use everything you've got.

Now Try This Question: 3 consecutive letters have been taken out of a word. Select which three letter word has been omitted, from the options. Write your answer below:

H___S

A. NOT   B. EEL   C. YET   D. BIN   E. POT

Answer: B, EEL

2) DECIPHERING WORDS

Three consecutive letters are removed from the word in CAPITALS. From the options, find the missing letters to complete the sentence.
Write your answer below:

LHER jackets are still in fashion today!

A. OSE
B. IGH
C. IHT
D. ENT
E. EAT

Answer and Explanation: E, EAT. Out of LOSEHER, LIGHHER, LIHTHER, LENTHER and LEATHER, only LEATHER is a real word. Substitute all of the options in to see which works. These questions are often harder than 'Removing Subset Words,' as many of the options create words that look real. However, these may be less off-putting as the three letter words in the other question type can be distracting.

Tips: Write out every single option if you are struggling, and eliminate the options that do not look like words. See if one word stands out to you as something that you recognise, and be sure to use the context of the sentence given to try and provoke your memory.

Now Try This Question: Three consecutive letters are removed from the word in CAPITALS. From the options, find the missing

letters to complete the sentence.
Write your answer below:

As soon as he got the ball he VOLLD it into the net!

A. EEE
B. EDE
C. EYE
D. END
E. EEP

Answer: C

3) REARRANGED WORDS

Sample Question: You are required to take one letter from the first word and move it to the second word, creating two new words. Write your answer below:

WHERE SEAT

Answer and Explanation: HERE SWEAT. This question assesses your child's ability to build new words, understand the similarities between words, and even break down words into their constituent parts. In this case, look at the first word, WHERE. Which letter can you take out to form a new word? Taking out W gives HERE, so this is one possibility. Taking out H gives WERE which is also a word. WHRE, WHEE, WHER are not words therefore we have W and H to add to the next word. Adding W gives SWEAT, which is a word. Trying to add H to any part of SEAT will not make a recognisable word, and so the answer is HERE and SWEAT.

Tips: Being systematic and taking out one letter at a time from the first option, and trying to add it to the second ensures you try all possible combinations, and do not miss the answer. Some words may seem odd outside the context of a sentence, but you must have faith in your vocabulary! Remember that there will only ever be one correct option.

Now Try This Question: You are required to take one letter from the first word and move it to the second word, creating two new words. Write your answer below:

THOSE CUE

Answer: HOSE CUTE

4) INCOMPLETE WORDS

Sample Question: Write the letter that will complete the word in front of the brackets and begin the word after the brackets. The SAME letter must fit into BOTH sets of brackets. Write your answer below:

tim (_) ach, can (_) asy

Answer and Explanation: E. Answering these questions is actually quite easy! Simply go through the alphabet one letter at a time, until you find a letter that fits all 4 words. Try A. Tima and aach are not words. Move onto B. Timb and bach are not words either. Move through the alphabet until you reach E. Tim(e)ach, can(e)asy. This method ensures you do not miss a letter. You must remember to check that the letter works in both sets of brackets.

Tips: You may just notice a letter that fits into both brackets immediately. If this is the case, then it is very convenient. However, when you go into the exam, you want to be sure you can get this question correct every time.

Having a method of running through the alphabet quickly will ensure that you never get this question wrong, as long as you are not careless!

Now Try This Question: Write the letter that will **complete** the word in front of the brackets and begin the word after the brackets. The SAME letter must fit into BOTH sets of brackets. Write your answer below:

gon (_) ate, han (_) ram

Answer: G. Gon(g)ate, han(g)ram

5) COMBINING WORDS

Sample Question: Find one word from each group that together makes **one correctly spelt word**. The letters **must not be rearranged**. The word from the first group must always be used first. Write your answer below:

I am (one, four, five) (child, teen, adult) years old.

A. Onechild

B. Fourchild

C. Fourteen

D. Oneadult

E. Fiveteen

Answer and Explanation: C, Fourteen. This question tests your ability to bring together two words, to create a brand new compound word. Reading the sentence gives you a hint as to what the word could be. It gives you context: the sentence is talking about how old someone is. Therefore, you would want to look for a number. Out of your 5 options, fourteen is the only possible answer.

Tips: Whilst you may be able to use the context of the sentence to get you to your answer, you could also try an alternative approach. Cover the sentence and look at your 5 options. Which one looks like a word? Onechild? Fourchild? Oneadult? Fiveteen? These are most definitely not words, and therefore the correct answer is Fourteen.

Now Try This Question: Find one word from each group that together makes **one correctly spelt word**. The letters must not be rearranged. The word from the first group must always be used first. Write your answer below:

(stroll, run, jog) (way, route, path)

A. Strollway

B. Jogroute

C. Runpath

D. Strollroute

E. Runway

Answer: E, Runway

6) COMMON WORD ASSOCIATIONS

Sample Question: The word in brackets is formed from the main word. **Identify the pattern** to work out the **missing word** from the options given. Write your answer below:

Catching (tin), diameter (ate), separate (?)

A. PET   B. RAT   C. PES   D. REP   E. PAT

Answer and Explanation: E, PAT. This question is assessing how to follow a pattern in the first two words, and apply it to the last word. From 'catching' the word 'tin' has been formed. The 3rd letter is 't', and 'in' are the 6th and 7th letters. This is the same for 'diameter', where the 3rd letter is 'a', and the 6th and 7th letters are 'te', forming 'ATE'. Here, for 'separate,' the answer would be 'PAT' by the same method.

Tips: Look at the first two words, and how the word in brackets was made from the word outside the brackets. It may be one chunk taken out of the word, or a certain pattern of letters. This will give you the method to solve the last, unknown bracket. When there are repeated letters in a word, keep track of which one you are working with.

Now Try This Question: In each case, the word in brackets is formed from the main word. **Identify the pattern** to work out the **missing word** from the options given. Write your answer below:

Sergeant (ran), provider (ode), pipeline (?)

A. LIP   B. NEP   C. PIN   D. PEL   E. PEEL

Answer: C

7) ALPHABET CODES

Sample Question: Work out the **relationship** between the word and the code to solve the code and write your answer below:

A B C D E F G H I J K L M N O P Q R S T U V W X Y Z

Your teachers organise a treasure hunt at your school.

They give you the following code to solve to find the treasure.

LOOP is to KMLL. What is the code for DRESS?

Answer and Explanation: CPBON. Use the code given within the question to formulated a method of finding the answer. LOOP is to KMLL. Look at the first letter from each word: L and K. From your alphabet you can see that you need to go one letter backwards from L to get to K. Now look at the second letters. O and M. From your alphabet, you can see you must move two letter backwards from O to get to M. Look at the third letters. O and L. This is 3 letters backwards from O. You should now be able to spot a pattern. For the first letter, you move one letter backwards. For the second letter you move two letters backwards and so on.

Now you must follow this same method for DRESS. Start with D. One letter backwards from D is C. Two letters backwards from R is P. Three letters backwards from E is B. Four letters backwards from S is O. Five letters backwards from S is N. Therefore, DRESS is converted to CPBON.

Tips: Be very methodical and do not assume that the

www.My11PlusPapers.co.uk

pattern used will be static for all letters, therefore make sure you convert ALL LETTERS before you move on to using the rules that you think you have determined. Some questions will ask you to DECODE answers, as below. Give it a go and see if you can solve it without help! It is best not to rush, but to take it slow and get it right the first time.

Now Try This Question: Work out the relationship between the word and the code to solve the code and write your answer below:

A B C D E F G H I J K L M N O P Q R S T U V W X Y Z

Your teachers organise a treasure hunt at your school. They give you the following code to solve to find the treasure.

LOOP is to KMLL. Decode the following: SUFNG

Answer: TWIRL

8) ALPHABET PUZZLES

Sample Question: Find the pair of letters that will complete the sentence in the best way. The alphabet is provided below to help you. Write your answer below:

A B C D E F G H I J K L M N O P Q R S T U V W X Y Z

CM is to AP as GT is to ___?

Answer and Explanation: EW. Look at how the first two letters were transformed into the second two letters. CM to AP. Start with the first letter of each. C to A. As you can see from the alphabet above, go backwards two letters from C, to get A. Now look at the second letters. M to P. Move 3 letters forward to go from M to P. Now apply this to the letters GT. From G, two letters backwards is E. From T, three letters forward is W. Therefore your answer is EW.

Tips: This question is similar to the Alphabet Codes style of question, and therefore should be treated similarly. Work out a method for getting from CM to AP, and apply this to GT. Always have a systematic method in mind.

Now Try This Question: Find the numbers and letters that will complete the sentence in the best way. The alphabet is provided below to help you. Write your answer below:

A B C D E F G H I J K L M N O P Q R S T U V W X Y Z

1F2G is to 3H4J as 1M2N is to ___?

Answer: 3O4Q

9) NUMBER CODES

Sample Question: In each set of numbers, the number in the brackets is related to the two numbers either side of it. Find this relation to work out the missing number '(?)' in the third set. Choose one of the option and write your answer below:

Example:

Q: 4 (6) 2, 12 (14) 2, 7 (?) 4
A: (?) = 11

Question:

18 (2) 6, 56 (6) 8, 66 (?) 6

A. 11   B. 15   C. 12   D. 10   E. 21

Answer and Explanation: D, 10. Look at the first group of 3 numbers: 18 (2) 6. Look for a pattern connecting the two numbers outside to the one inside. Think of multiplication, division, addition and subtraction. If you are not sure, move onto the second group. 56 (6) 8. Looking at the first group, you may notice that 18 divided by 6 is 3. This number is one more than the number in the brackets, 2. The same method also fits with the second group. 56 divided by 8 is 7. This number is one more that the number in brackets, 6. For the last group, 66 divided by 6 is 11. 11-1 = 10. This means that your answer is D, 10.

Tips: This question relies on you spotting mathematical patterns, again by applying your 4 mathematical pillars: multiplication, division, addition and subtraction. If you are stuck trying to spot a pattern, try all of these individually. If you cannot solve it still, try combining a mix of 2 or more together to target those more challenging questions.

Now Try This Question: In each set of numbers, the number in the brackets is related to the two numbers either side of it. Find this relation to work out the missing number '(?)' in the third set. Choose one of the options and write your answer below:

Question:

12 (19) 4, 7 (15) 5, 8 (?) 1

A. 17   B. 5   C. 12   D. 25   E. 9

Answer: C

10) WORD RELATIONS

Sample Question: Select the two words inside the brackets that are connected in some way to the words outside the brackets. Write your answer below:

Ryan only likes certain types of boats. He likes the SPEEDBOAT, YACHT (canoe, bicycle, car, dinghy, plane) and many more.

Answer and Explanation: Canoe and Dinghy. This question tests your ability to identify patterns between groups of words. Here, the question has helped you, but this will not always be the case. You know that Ryan only likes certain types of boats. Two types are speedboats and yachts. From the 5 options, which of the others could also be types of boats? A canoe? Yes. A bicycle, car or plane? Most definitely not. Even if you do not know what a dinghy is, logically it should be the other option, since none of the others make sense. Therefore, your answer would be canoe and dinghy.

Tips: Some questions will not give you a hint at the beginning, and you will need to identify a pattern between the first two words outside the brackets without further context. Read the 5 options, and cross out ones that either mean the opposite or simply do not fit the pattern.

Now Try This Question: Select the two words inside the brackets that are connected in some way to the words outside the brackets. Write your answer below:

HURRY RUSH (slow, urgent, haste, carry, hinder)

Answer: Urgent and Haste

11) SIMILES

Select the word from the brackets that will **complete the sentence in the most sensible way**.
Write your answer below:

Open is to SHOW as close is to (door, lock, hide)

Answer and Explanation: Hide. These questions test your ability to understand the relationships between different words. To get to the answer, you need to understand how open relates to show, how open relates to close, and how show relates to a word in the brackets. Open and close are opposites, and so we are looking for the opposite of show, which is hide. Additionally, when you open something, you show the contents of it. Likewise, when you close something, you hide the contents of it.

Tips: Many students only look at the association between the first words (open and show, here) and then try to apply that to the second part of the sentence. You should instead look at the connections between all of the words, as described in the explainer above. Remember that there are two ways of getting to the answer. Often the words in the brackets may be similar, as is the case here wherein lock and hide are along the same lines. You should use both comparisons (eg. open to show as well as open to close) to figure out the best answer. These questions are dependent on having a good vocabulary, so get training!

Now Try This Question: Select the word from the brackets that will complete the sentence in the most sensible way. Write your answer below:

Secret is to HIDE as disclose is to (reveal, shut, tale)

Answer: Reveal

12) LETTER SEQUENCES

Sample Question: Find the pair of letters that will continue the series. The alphabet is provided below to help you. Write your answer below:

A B C D E F G H I J K L M N O P Q R S T U V W X Y Z

UF, XH, AJ, DL, GN, ___?

Answer and Explanation: JP. This is a letter sequence, therefore the letters all follow a particular pattern. Look at the first letter of each part of the sequence. U --> X --> A --> D --> G. Next, look at the alphabet and you will notice that there are 2 letters between each of the terms: U (VW) X (YZ) A (BC) D (EF) G (HI) J. Using this method we have found the first letter of our answer, J.

Now look at the last letter of each part of the sequence. F --> H --> J --> L --> N. Using the same technique as before, look for a pattern connecting all these letters: F (G) H (I) J (K) L (M) N (O) P. We have found the second part of our answer, P. Our answer is therefore JP.

Tips: For these questions, it often helps to split the two letters of each term of the sequence, and try to work out the pattern of the first letters together, and then the second letters together. However, sometimes you will need to look at them as a whole to gain a proper understanding of what is happening. As for all puzzles that require you to study the alphabet, you should not worry about taking your time as it's important to make sure that you get it correct the first time round. Being one letter away from the correct answer means that you don't get the mark. It is often helpful to draw small loops between the letters when counting to help keep track.

Now Try This Question:

Sample Question: Find the pair of letters that will continue the series. The alphabet is provided below to help you. Write your answer below:

A B C D E F G H I J K L M N O P Q R S T U V W X Y Z

FT, CV, ZX, WZ, TB, ___?

Answer: QD

13) NUMBER SEQUENCES

Sample Question: Find the number that best complete the series. Fill in the missing blank with one of the following options and write your answer below:

2, 6, 18, ____, 162

A. 18   B. 34   C. 28   D. 54   E. 40

Answer and Explanation: D, 54. This is because between 2 and 6, there is a difference of 4. Between 6 and 18 there is also a difference of 12. It logically follows that the differences between the numbers in the sequence seem to be progressively tripling. 4 is multiplied by 3 to get 12. You can see that 12 x 3 = 36. Let us test to see if this works. 12 + 36 = 54. 36 x 3 = 108. 108 + 54 = 162, which is the final number in the sequence. We have confirmed that D, 54, is the correct answer.

Tips: Sequences act to test your child's ability to apply logic and identify patterns. Always think to yourself, what is the pattern between these numbers?

Use your four pillars of mathematics to help break down the problem if you are stuck.

- *Addition*
- *Subtraction*
- *Multiplication*
- *Division*

Do the sequences follow any of these patterns? If not, you could consider using square or cube numbers, or a combination of all of the above.

Now Try This Question: Find the number that best complete the series. Fill in the missing blank with one of the following options and write your answer below:

3, 4, 6, 10, 18, ____

A. 24   B. 30   C. 32   D. 34   E. 36

Answer: D

Question Type-Ordered Walkthrough

Secondary Entrance

14) OPPOSITES

Sample Question: Select the pair of words, one from each group, that are opposite in meaning to each other, from the options given below. Write your answer below:

The opposite of (Little, Real, Thirsty) is (Tired, Hungry, Quenched).

A.   Little Tired

B.   Real Hungry

C.   Thirsty Hungry

D.   Thirsty Tired

E.   Thirsty Quenched

Answer and Explanation: E, Thirsty Quenched. This type of question tests your understanding of a particular word's definition, and how to apply this to work out words which mean the opposite. To begin, look at your first 3 words. The opposite of 'little' is big, which is not an option. The opposite of 'real' is unreal, which is also not an option. The opposite of 'thirsty' is something meaning not being thirsty. You may not know the word for this, but not being thirsty most definitely does not mean 'tired', or 'hungry'. Therefore, you are left with the word 'quenched', which does in fact mean the opposite of thirsty.

Tips: You may not know the meaning of all of the words you are presented with. Use logic and reasoning to try to find the best fit, and eliminate answers you know for sure are not correct. This way you learn from your mistakes, and build your vocabulary at the same time!

Now Try This Question: Select the pair of words, one from each group, that are opposite in meaning to each other, from the options given. Write your answer below:

The opposite of (Onward, Jump, Together) is (Allow, Fight, Alone).

A.   Onward Allow

B.   Jump Fight

C.   Together Allow

D.   Together Alone

E.   Jump Alone

Answer: D

15) DIFFERENTIATING WORDS

Sample Question: Select the TWO odd words from the options given. Write your answer below:

Rain, Faint, Pain, Paint, Saint.

A.   Paint Faint

B.   Rain Pain

C.   Saint Paint

D.   Paint Rain

E.   Pain Saint

Answer and Explanation: B, Rain Pain. This question tests your ability to look at a group of words, and work out which two words do not fit in with the rest. They may be different in grammar, definition or just the pattern of letters. In this case, all the words end in either '–ain', or '–aint'. 'Faint', 'Paint' and 'Saint'. Both 'Rain' and 'Pain' do not end in '–t', and so are the odd words in this case.

Tips: Remember that finding the odd words out may not just be on what they mean. Look for patterns in the letters, and the order of these letters too, especially if there is no obvious pattern as to what they mean. For example, they may all start or end with a certain letter.

Now Try This Question: Select the TWO odd words from the options given. Write your answer below:

Think, Query, Believe, Understand, Confuse, Acknowledge

A.   Think Confuse

B.   Believe Understand

C.   Confuse Believe

D.   Think Understand

E.   Query Confuse

Answer: E

16) VERBAL MATHS PROBLEMS

Sample Question: Choose the correct answer for the following problem. Write your answer below:

When a number is added to 34, the answer is 6 more than nine multiplied by four. What is the number?

A. 12   B. 6   C. 3   D. 8   E. 14

Answer and Explanation: D, 8. This question may seem odd in a Verbal Reasoning paper as it is maths, however, the ability to convert a question written in words into numbers is an important skill. In this case a number has been added to 34. The answer to this number is 6 more than 9 multiplied by 4. What sum can do you do straight away? $9 \times 4 = 36$. The answer to 6 more than this is $36 + 6 = 42$. Which number, when added to 34 gives you 42? If you take 34 from 42 you will get the answer: $42 - 34 = 8$.

Tips: Most students trip up when forming multiple sums, one after the other. Knowing how to create an equation takes practice - you should follow a logical manner and make sure that you check your answers at the end. Verbal Reasoning maths questions vary the sums and types of maths you need to use. However, they all have one thing in common: they require you to make a wordy question into a maths sum, so be sure to give this plenty of practice in advance of the exam!

Now Try This Question: Choose the correct answer for the following problem. Write your answer below:

When 15 is multiplied by a number, the answer is four less than when eight is multiplied by eight. What is the number?

A. 8   B. 3   C. 9   D. 2   E. 4

Answer: E

17) PRACTICAL MATHS PROBLEMS

Read the information provided and choose the single best answer for the question. Write your answer below:

5 friends decide to take part in a charity run. Harun runs 15 miles, whilst Aaron runs 2 miles less. Jacob runs 3 miles more than Aaron. Michael and Wenger both ran 1 more mile than Aaron. Who ran the most miles?

A. Harun
B. Aaron
C. Jacob
D. Michael
E. Wenger

Answer and Explanation: C, Jacob. Harun runs 15 miles. Aaron runs 2 miles less than this, 15 - 2 = 13 miles. Jacob runs 3 miles more than Aaron, 13 + 3 = 16 miles. Michael and Wenger run 1 mile more than Aaron, 13 + 1 = 14 miles. The largest distance here is 16 miles, run by Jacob. This type of question tests your ability to understand a real life situation and solve a mathematical problem within this situation.

Tips: There will often be a lot of words which are conveying a relatively small amount of content. Try and filter out the core numbers here: 15, 2, 3 and 1, then figure out what sums you are going to be doing with them. Make sure to relate any calculated answers back to the individuals that they concern. If it helps, make a table with names and distances, when you calculate how far someone ran you can input this data in an organised way.

Now Try This Question: Read the information provided and choose the single best answer for the question. Write your answer below:

Megan, Julia and Amanda run a relay race. Amanda completed her part of the relay in 31 seconds. Julia finished her part 5 seconds quicker than Amanda, whilst Megan took 14 seconds longer than Amanda to complete her part. How long did the entire relay take?

A. 60 seconds
B. 102 seconds
C. 50 seconds
D. 81 seconds
E. 73 seconds

Answer: C

18) FUNCTIONS

Sample Question: Choose the correct answer by completing the following equation with the correct sign as appropriate. Write your answer below:

(560 ÷ 10 x 2) ___ 2 = 8 x 7 ÷ 1

A. +   B. -   C. x   D. ÷

Answer and Explanation: D, ÷. This is a BODMAS / BIDMAS style maths question. Head over to the Maths syllabus for more help on these types of questions. In this case, look at the brackets first: (560 ÷ 10 x 2). This is 112 as 560 ÷ 10 = 56 and 56 x 2 = 112. Move over to the other side of the sum: 8 x 7 ÷ 1 = 56. Therefore 112 ? 2 = 56. We already know that 56 x 2 is 112, and so if you divide it by two, you would get 56 again. Therefore the answer is D, ÷.

Tips: These questions will continually test your understanding of BODMAS or BIDMAS, The Verbal Reasoning element is the ability to use symbols correctly. Furthermore, remember that letters can easily represent numbers, but that the laws of mathematics remain the same, so do not be phased by the presence of letters. You should treat them just as you would numbers. Many people find it helpful to rewrite the entire sum with brackets added in to clarify which sums are going to be done in which order.

Now Try This Question: Choose the correct answer by completing the following equation with the correct sign as appropriate. Write your answer below:

93 + 3 x 3 = (47 + 4) x 4 ___ 2

A. +   B. -   C. x   D. ÷

Answer: D

19) ALGEBRAIC EQUATIONS

Using the provided code, complete the following sums writing your answer in <u>letters</u>:

a = 5, b = 7, c = 3, d = 2, e = 8

What is: (a + b) ÷ (c × d) = ___?

Answer and Explanation: d. a + b is 5 + 7 = 12. c × d is 3 × 2 = 6. 12 ÷ 6 = 2. As a letter, this is d. Make sure to give your answer as a letter! It is an extremely common mistake that students write down the number they have calculated instead of the letter, contrary to what is asked for. In this question, it is important to follow BODMAS / BIDMAS. First, do the sums inside the brackets, then do the division between the two sums afterwards. Here, it is especially important not to neglect the brackets, as without the brackets a + b would be lower down in the priority when doing the calculation, which would result in a different answer.

Tips: Many students, despite it being underlined, forget to put their answers in letters. There will be a few questions in whatever exam you sit that really test your ability to read the information carefully. Do not lose focus. Secondly, make sure to follow BODMAS / BIDMAS on a question like this, and do not worry that you are mixing numbers and letters – letters behave exactly as numbers do. Keep in mind that certain abbreviations exist, however. For example, you may see c × d written as cd. This is the sort of question where there are lots of little tricks to be aware of.

Now Try This Question: Using the provided code, complete the following sums writing your answer in <u>letters</u>:

a = 5, b = 7, c = 3, d = 2, e = 8

What is: b × d – c – e = ___?

Answer: C

20) HIDDEN WORDS

Sample Question: A four letter word is hidden between two words in the sentence below. These **two words are always next to each other**, but there may be punctuation between them. Find this **four letter word** from one of the options. Write your chosen option below:

Example:

Q. Tom kicked the ball over the fence.
A. Love = ball over

Question:

It was slightly painful to get two extra injections before I travel on holiday.

A.   before I

B.   extra injections

C.   painful to

D.   get an

E.   two extra

Answer and Explanation: B, extra injections. These questions test your vocabulary of words, and to think outside of the box and spot hidden words. Look at your sentence, and look between each word. "It was" are the first two words. Join them together and see if you can find a word. Itwas. Twas could be considered an old English word, however it would be written as 'twas and is therefore not acceptable. The next two words are 'was slightly'. There are no words when you join these together. As you move through each word systematically, you reach 'extra injection'. Extrainjection. Here you can see a word, 'rain', formed between the two. This is the answer, B.

Tips: Go through each part of the sentence two words at a time, and look at the combination of 3 letters from the first word and 1 from the second word. Next, 2 letters from each, and then 1 letter from the first word and 3 letters from the second word. This way you cannot miss the answer, as long as you are not careless of course! You will get faster and faster at this screening process with practice.

Now Try This Question: A four letter word is hidden between two words in the sentence below. These **two words are always next to each other**, but there **may be punctuation between** them. Find this **four letter word** from one of the options. Write your chosen option below.

Question:

A trip to a spa involves having a meal with friends as well.

A.   trip to

B.   having a

C.   friends as

D.   meal with

E.   spa involves

Answer: E

Verbal Reasoning - Test 1

Time allowed for this paper : 60 minutes

Instructions for Best Practice:

> Attempt all of the questions.
> Ensure that your answers are clearly marked in the answer boxes.
> Calculators and rulers must not be used.
> Equipment recommended: 2 x Pencil & 1 x Eraser.

Verbal Reasoning - Test 1

Marks

1) Three consecutive letters have been taken out of a word. Select which three letters **have been omitted** from the options. Write your answer below:

He carried the B____ET all the way up the hill.

A. END
B. ASK
C. AGO
D. ANT
E. THE

Answer:

6) **Find the pair of letters** that will continue the series. The alphabet is provided below to help you. Write your answer below:

A B C D E F G H I J K L M N O P Q R S T U V W X Y Z

QQ is to NK as HH is to ___?

Answer:

2) Find the pair of letters and numbers that will continue the series. The alphabet is provided below to help you. Write your answer below:

A B C D E F G H I J K L M N O P Q R S T U V W X Y Z

11AY, 22BX, 33CW, 44DV, 55EU, ___?

Answer:

7) Select the TWO odd words from the options given. Write your answer below:

Black, king, purple, green, house

Answer:

3) A four letter word is hidden between two words in the sentence below. These two words are always next to each other, but there may be punctuation between them. Find this four letter word from one of the 5 options.

Question: The bird made the nest beautiful.

A. The bird   D. the nest
B. bird made   E. nest beautiful
C. made the

Answer:

8) Select the TWO odd words from the options given. Write your answer below:

House, office, tractor, bungalow, chimney

Answer:

4) Choose the correct answer by **completing the following** functions and sums with the **correct numbers and signs** as appropriate. Write your answer below:

22 add another number equals 41. What is the other number?

A. 16
B. 19
C. 27
D. 22
E. 25

Answer:

9) You are required to **move one letter from the first word** to the second word, creating two new words. Write your answer below:

GATE OLD

Answer:

5) Using the provided code, complete the following sums writing your answer in <u>numbers</u>:

If a = 5, b = 1, c = 2, d = 9, e = 3

$e \div b = $ ___?

Answer:

10) Choose the correct answer by completing the following functions and sums with the correct numbers and signs as appropriate. Write your answer below:

Which of the following equal the addition of 25% of 12 to 20% of 15:

A. 6
B. 8
C. 18
D. 5
E. 7

Answer:

Verbal Reasoning

15

Marks

11) Choose the correct answer for the following problem. Write your answer below:

Christmas Day is on Friday.
Three days after tomorrow is Christmas Day.

Which ONE of the following statements must be true?

A. Today is Sunday
B. The day before yesterday was Saturday
C. Tomorrow will be Wednesday
D. Today is Thursday
E. Tomorrow is Saturday

Answer:

12) Find one word from each group that together makes one correctly spelt word. The letters must not be rearranged. The word from the first group must always be used first.

Write your answer below:

The young man was truly (hand, foot, finger) (same, some, sat).

Answer:

13) Find one word from each group that together makes one correctly spelt word. The letters must not be rearranged. The word from the first group must always be used first. Write your answer below:

The (day, week, month) (start, finish, end) is nearly here!

Answer:

14) Work out the relationship between the word and the code to solve the code and write your answer below:

A B C D E F G H I J K L M N O P Q R S T U V W X Y Z

Your teachers organise a treasure hunt at your school. They give you the following code to solve, to find the treasure.

BASKET is to DCUMGV.

What is the code for BICYCLE?

Answer:

15) Choose the correct answer for the following problem. Write your answer below:

$72 - 18 = 9 \times \_\_$

A. 3
B. 4
C. 5
D. 6
E. 7

Answer:

16) Select the word from the brackets that will **complete the sentence in the most sensible way**. Write your answer below:

Start is to BEGIN as end is to (less, finish, start)

Answer:

17) You are required to **move one letter from the first word to the second word**, creating two new words. Write your answer below:

TABLE READ

Answer:

18) In each set of numbers, the number in the brackets is related to **the two numbers either side of it**. Find this **relation** to work out the missing number '(?)' in the third set. Choose one of the options and write your answer below:

1 (5) 4, 6 (10) 4, 5 (?) 2

A. 1
B. 15
C. 18
D. 7
E. 9

Answer:

19) A four letter word is hidden between two words in the sentence below. These **two words** are always next to each other, but there may be punctuation between them. Find this **four letter word** from one of the options. Write your answer below:

The bird ate the bread given by my sister.

A. bird ate   D. bread given
B. ate the   E. my sister
C. the bread

Answer:

20) Three consecutive letters have been taken out of a word. Which three letters have been omitted from the options given? Write your answer below:

The ____EST expanded across the horizon.

A. DON
B. DOG
C. FOR
D. BUY
E. DIG

Answer:

Marks

21) Three consecutive letters are removed from the word in CAPITALS. From the options, find the missing letters to complete the sentence. Write your answer below:

Ross carried his shopping in a BET

A. AGO
B. ASK
C. ANT
D. THE
E. END

Answer:

26) Select the word from the brackets that will complete the sentence in the most sensible way. Write your answer below:

Up is to DOWN as forward is to (backward, right, up)

Answer:

22) Work out the relationship between the word and the code to solve the code and write your answer below:

A B C D E F G H I J K L M N O P Q R S T U V W X Y Z

Your teachers organise a treasure hunt at your school. They give you the following code to solve, to find the treasure.

BASKET is to DCUMGV.

What is the code for COURT?

Answer:

27) Find the pair of letters that will continue the series. The alphabet is provided below to help you. Write your answer below:

A B C D E F G H I J K L M N O P Q R S T U V W X Y Z

BC is to GH as MN is to ___?

Answer:

23) Read the information provided and choose the single best answer for the question. Write your answer below:

Ben usually goes to visit his friend on Friday. Today is Thursday.

Which ONE of the following statements must be true?

A. Ben went to visit his friend today
B. Ben went to visit his friend yesterday
C. Ben will visit his friend tomorrow
D. Tomorrow will be Friday
E. Yesterday was Monday

Answer:

28) In each sentence, three consecutive letters are removed from the word in CAPITALS. From the options, find the missing letters to complete the sentence. Write your answer below:

Aparna wore her PL necklace to the ball.

A. EYE
B. TOE
C. EAR
D. URN
E. EAT

Answer:

24) Find the pair of letters that will continue the series. The alphabet is provided below to help you. Write your answer below:

A B C D E F G H I J K L M N O P Q R S T U V W X Y Z

CE, GI, KM, OQ, SU, ___?

Answer:

29) The words in brackets are formed from the main word. Identify the pattern to work out the missing word from the options given. Write your answer below:

Playing (pin), standing (sin), talking (?)

A. LIN
B. GIN
C. SIN
D. TIN
E. KIN

Answer:

25) In each set of numbers, the number in the brackets is related to the two numbers either side of it. Find this relation to work out the missing number '(?)' in the third set. Choose one of the options and write your answer below:

2 (8) 6, 5 (9) 4, 5 (?) 13

A. 18
B. 4
C. 12
D. 21
E. 17

Answer:

30) Find the number that best completes the series. Fill in the missing blank with one of the following options and write your answer below:

1, 2, 3, ___

A. 7
B. 6
C. 5
D. 4
E. 3

Answer:

31) Select the two words **inside the brackets** that are connected in some way to the words **outside the brackets**. Write your answer below:

James only likes certain types of crockery. He likes the SPOON, CUP (plate, table, chair, fork, mat)

Answer:

36) The words in brackets are formed from the main word. Identify the pattern to work out the missing word from the options given. Write your answer below:

Bat (pat), best (pest), bun (?)

A. NUN   D. BUN
B. BEST   E. PEST
C. PUN

Answer:

32) Select the two words **inside the brackets** that are connected in some way to the words **outside the brackets**:

Fiona only uses certain types of transport. She uses the BUS, TRAIN (coach, tram, tractor, station, bike)

Answer:

37) Write the letter that will complete the word in front of the brackets and begin the word after the brackets. The SAME letter must fit into BOTH sets of brackets. Write your answer below:

pas (_) alt, tos (_) ulk

Answer:

33) Choose the correct answer by completing the following functions and sums with the correct numbers and signs as appropriate. Write your answer below:

4 × 12 = 73 – ___

A. 31
B. 45
C. 25
D. 16
E. 19

Answer:

38) Find the numbers that best complete the series. Fill in the missing blank with one of the following options and write your answer below:

2, 4, 6, 8, ___

A. 5
B. 9
C. 14
D. 10
E. 6

Answer:

34) Using the provided code, complete the following sums writing your answer in numbers:

If a = 5, b = 1, c = 2, d = 9, e = 3

Solve: a × c = ___?

Answer:

39) Select the pair of words, one from each group that are opposite in meaning to each other from the options given below. Write your answer below:

The opposite of (fat, short, slim) is (strong, heavy, tall).

A. Fat strong
B. Short tall
C. Slim heavy
D. Short strong
E. Fat heavy

Answer:

35) Write the letter that will complete the word in front of the brackets and begin the word after the brackets. The SAME letter must fit into BOTH sets of brackets. Write your answer below:

cos (_) ram, raf (_) oll

Answer:

40) Select the pair of words, one from each group that are opposite in meaning to each other from the options given below. Write your answer below:

The opposite of (discover, find, treasure) is (lose, trail, map).

A. Discover trail
B. Treasure map
C. Find lose
D. Discover lose
E. Find trail

Answer:

www.My11PlusPapers.co.uk

Verbal Reasoning - Test 2

Time allowed for this paper : 60 minutes

Instructions for Best Practice:

> Attempt all of the questions.
> Ensure that your answers are clearly marked in the answer boxes.
> Calculators and rulers must not be used.
> Equipment recommended: 2 x Pencil & 1 x Eraser.

Verbal Reasoning - Test 2

1) In each set of numbers, the number in the brackets is related to the two numbers either side of it. Find this relation to work out the missing number '(?)' in the third set. Choose one of the five options below.

4 (8) 4, 3 (6) 3, 6 (?) 6

A. 12
B. 24
C. 7
D. 2
E. 13

Answer:

2) Find the pair of letters that will continue the series. The alphabet is provided below to help you. Write your answer below:

A B C D E F G H I J K L M N O P Q R S T U V W X Y Z

XD, YE, ZF, AG, BH, ___?

Answer:

3) Find one word from each group that together makes one correctly spelt word. The letters must not be rearranged. The word from the first group must always be used first. Write your answer below:

The (paper, card, sheet) (table, surface, board) box was under the table.

A. Cardtable   D. Sheetsurface
B. Cardboard   E. Papertable
C. Papersurface

Answer:

4) Three consecutive letters have been taken out of a word. Select which three letters have been omitted from the options. Write your answer below:

The CH____ER was caught half way through the card game.

A. EEL
B. EAR
C. BUS
D. EAT
E. EYE

Answer:

5) Using the provided code, complete the following sums writing your answers in numbers.

Write your answer below:

a = 8, b = 0, c = 4, d = 2, e = 7

Solve: e + d = ___?

Answer:

6) You are required to move one letter from the first word to the second word, creating two new words. Write your answer below:

COAT BED

Answer:

7) Work out the relationship between the word and the code to solve the code and write your answer below:

A B C D E F G H I J K L M N O P Q R S T U V W X Y Z

BASKET is to DCUMGV. Decode the following: DQCV.

(Hint: Decode is the opposite of code.)

Answer:

8) Using the provided code, complete the following sums writing your answers in numbers.

a = 5, b = 1, c = 2, d = 9, e = 3.

Solve: d ÷ e × c − b = ___?

Answer:

9) Select the letter that will complete the word in front of the brackets and begin the word after the brackets. The SAME letter must fit into BOTH sets of brackets. Write your answer below:

ban (_) eep, lac (_) ick

Answer:

10) Select the two words inside the brackets that are connected in some way to the words outside the brackets.

Write your answer below:

MOTHER BROTHER (friend, father, colleague, baby, sister)

Answer:

www.My11PlusPapers.co.uk

Marks

11) Select the letter that will complete the word in front of the brackets and begin the word after the brackets. The SAME letter must fit into BOTH sets of brackets. Write your answer below:

bel (_) ail, mal (_) alk

Answer:

12) Select the two words inside the brackets that are connected in some way to the words outside the brackets. Write your answer below:

James only likes certain types of electronics. He likes the COMPUTER, PHONE (television, ball, racket, toy, camera)

Answer:

13) Select the word from the brackets that will complete the sentence in the most sensible way. Write your answer below:

Red is to APPLE as yellow is to (orange, pear, banana)

Answer:

14) Find one word from each group that together makes one correctly spelt word. The letters must not be rearranged. The word from the first group must always be used first. Write your answer below:

My (bed, cupboard, table) (roof, room, garden) is so colourful!

A. Cupboardroom
B. Tablegarden
C. Bedroom
D. Bedroof
E. Tableroof

Answer:

15) Select the word from the brackets that will complete the sentence in the most sensible way. Write your answer below:

Water is to SEA as sand is to (park, water, beach)

Answer:

16) Find the pair of letters that will complete the sentence in the best way. The alphabet is provided below to help you. Write your answer below:

A B C D E F G H I J K L M N O P Q R S T U V W X Y Z

CK is to EI as AI is to ___?

Answer:

17) Find the pair of letters that will complete the sentence in the best way. The alphabet is provided below to help you. Write your answer below:

A B C D E F G H I J K L M N O P Q R S T U V W X Y Z

OJ is to RK as MH is to ___?

Answer:

18) Select the pair of words, one from each group that are opposite in meaning to each other from the options given below. Write your answer below:
The opposite of (dawn, wake, early) is (late, sunrise, stop).

A. Dawn sunrise
B. Early stop
C. Wake sunrise
D. Wake late
E. Early late

Answer:

19) Select the TWO odd words from the options given below. Write your answer below:

Dinghy, horse, yacht, canoe, bicycle, ship, boat

A. Horse yacht
B. Canoe dinghy
C. Horse bicycle
D. Canoe bicycle
E. Yacht dinghy

Answer:

20) Select the TWO odd words from the options given below. Write your answer below:

Lemonade, tea, cheese, milk, bread, water, juice

A. Cheese bread
B. Milk cheese
C. Tea milk
D. Lemonade tea
E. Tea bread

Answer:

Marks

---

21) Work out the **relationship** between the word and the code to solve the code. Write your answer below:

A B C D E F G H I J K L M N O P Q R S T U V W X Y Z

Your teachers organise a treasure hunt. They give you the following code to help you find the treasure.

BASKET is to DCUMGV.

Decode the following: ECVEJ.

Answer:

---

22) Complete the following functions and sums with the **correct numbers and signs** as appropriate. Write your answer below:

9 + ___ = 7 x 3

A. 14
B. 12
C. 16
D. 22
E. 21

Answer:

---

23) Select the pair of words, one from each group that are **opposite** in meaning to each other from the options given below. Write your answer below:
The opposite of (accident, fire, dangerous) is (emergency, safe, police).

A. Accident emergency
B. Fire safe
C. Dangerous police
D. Dangerous safe
E. Fire police

Answer:

---

24) Choose the correct answer for the following problem. Write your answer below:

What number is 4 more than $\frac{1}{5}$ of 15?

A. 12
B. 11
C. 9
D. 7
E. 4

Answer:

---

25) Choose the correct answer for the following problem. Write your answer below:

Jack is taller than Amy but shorter than Simon. Patrick is taller than Amy but shorter than Jack. Minnie is shorter than Amy.
Who is tallest?

A. Jack
B. Amy
C. Simon
D. Patrick
E. Minnie

Answer:

---

26) You are required to **move one letter from the first word to the second word**, creating two new words.

SHARE CARE

Answer:

---

27) The words in brackets are formed from the main word. Identify the pattern to work out the **missing word** from the 5 options given below. Write your answer below:

Water (rat), bonds (son), magician (?)

A. CIA
B. NAG
C. GIC
D. MAG
E. GAN

Answer:

---

28) The words in brackets are formed from the main word. Identify the pattern to work out the **missing word** from the 5 options given below. Write your answer below:

Space (ace), together (her), cabin (?)

A. CAB
B. ABI
C. NAB
D. BIN
E. CIN

Answer:

---

29) Three consecutive letters are removed from the word in CAPITALS. These letters make a word. From the five options below, find the missing letters to complete the sentence . Write your answer below:

Paul did his work on the COMER.

A. HIM
B. HAM
C. HUT
D. BUT
E. PUT

Answer:

---

30) Three consecutive letters have been taken out of a word. Select which three letters have been omitted from the options. Write your answer below:

The young boy could not help but FR____ when made to eat his vegetables.

A. OUT
B. OAT
C. OWN
D. URN
E. EAT

Answer:

22

www.My11PlusPapers.co.uk

Marks

31) In each set of numbers, the number in the brackets is related to the two numbers either side of it. Find this relation to work out the missing number '(?)' in the third set. Choose one of the five options below and write your answer below.

5 (12) 7, 5 (14) 9, 6 (?) 4

A. 10
B. 13
C. 15
D. 16
E. 7

Answer:

32) A four letter word is hidden between two words in the sentence below. These two words are always next to each other, but there may be punctuation between them. Find this four letter word from one of the 5 options. Write your answer below:

What a deal! Socks and flip flops are now half price!

A. deal socks   D. are now
B. socks and   E. now half
C. half price

Answer:

33) Find the number that best completes the series. Fill in the missing blank with one of the following five options and write your answer below:

11, 13, 15, 17, 19, ___

A. 24
B. 21
C. 23
D. 28
E. 26

Answer:

34) Find the pair of letters that will continue the series. The alphabet is provided below to help you.

A B C D E F G H I J K L M N O P Q R S T U V W X Y Z

TS, SR, RQ, QP, PO, ___?

Answer:

35) Choose the correct answer for the following problem. Write your answer below:

What number is 7 more than 12 plus 6?

A. 25
B. 27
C. 33
D. 31
E. 29

Answer:

36) Complete the following functions and sums with the correct numbers and signs as appropriate. Write your answer below:

49 ÷ 7 = ___ ÷ 4

A. 8
B. 16
C. 28
D. 32
E. 64

Answer:

37) Three consecutive letters are removed from the word in CAPITALS. These letters make a word. From the five options below, find the missing letters to complete the sentence. Write your answer below:

Justin was talking on the PH.

A. ALL
B. EAR
C. EAT
D. ONE
E. ACE

Answer:

38) Choose the correct answer for the following problem. Write your answer below:

Jack is taller than Amy but shorter than Simon. Patrick is taller than Amy but shorter than Jack. Minnie is shorter than Amy.

Who is shortest?

A. Jack   D. Patrick
B. Amy   E. Minnie
C. Simon

Answer:

39) A four letter word is hidden between two words in the sentence below. These two words are always next to each other, but there may be punctuation between them. Find this four letter word from one of the 5 options.

I was surprised how all of the questions were easy to answer!

A. surprised how
B. how all
C. questions were
D. easy to
E. to answer

Answer:

40) Find the number that best completes the series. Fill in the missing blank with one of the following five options. Write your answer below:

5, 10, 15, 20, ___

A. 30
B. 25
C. 20
D. 27
E. 35

Answer:

www.My11PlusPapers.co.uk

Verbal Reasoning - Test 3

Time allowed for this paper : 60 minutes

Instructions for Best Practice:

> Attempt all of the questions.
> Ensure that your answers are clearly marked in the answer boxes.
> Calculators and rulers must not be used.
> Equipment recommended: 2 x Pencil & 1 x Eraser.

Verbal Reasoning - Test 3

1) Find the option that best completes the series. Fill in the missing blank with one of the following five options:

10 sweets, 14 sweets, 22 sweets, 34 sweets, ___?

A. 40 sweets
B. 64 sweets
C. 50 sweets
D. 55 sweets
E. 38 sweets

Answer:

2) Select the pair of words, one from each group, that are opposite in meaning to each other:

The opposite of (reliable, good, bad) is (friend, untrustworthy, relation).

A. Reliable and relation
B. Reliable and untrustworthy
C. Bad and untrustworthy
D. Good and friend
E. Bad and friend

Answer:

3) Find one word from each group that together makes one correctly spelt word. The letters must not be rearranged. The word from the first group must always be used first:

My (window, handle, door) (needle, knob, notch) needs to be polished soon!

A. Windownotch
B. Doorknob
C. Handleknob
D. Doornotch
E. Handleneedle

Answer:

4) Select the two words from the list that are connected in some way to the words in CAPITALS:

Dennis likes only certain types of sports. Two of them are TENNIS and FOOTBALL. Which other TWO does he like from the list?

cricket, basketball, sailing, karate, swimming

Answer:

5) Three consecutive letters have been taken out of a word in the sentence. Which three letters have been omitted:

The DECO____ION around the hall was absolutely splendid!

Answer:

6) Find the letters and numbers that will complete the sentence in the best way. The alphabet is provided below to help you:

A B C D E F G H I J K L M N O P Q R S T U V W X Y Z

Mr Martin wrote a code out for his class to solve. Can you solve it?

1L2M is to 1Q2R as 1A2B is to ___?

Answer:

7) You are required to move one letter from the first word to the second word, creating two new words. These will then complete the sentence.

POST AND

We will need the ____ and _____ to build the sandcastle.

Answer:

8) Work out the relationship between the word and the code to solve the code:

A B C D E F G H I J K L M N O P Q R S T U V W X Y Z

You are on a treasure hunt at school and your teacher gave you the following code to solve.

HOUSE = GMROZ.

What is the code for BED?

Answer:

9) Using the provided code, complete the following sums writing your answers in numbers:

apple = 8, ball = 0, car = 4, dog = 2, elephant = 7

Solve: apple − ball = ____?

Answer:

10) Using the provided code, complete the following sums writing your answers in numbers:

apple = 8, ball = 0, car = 4, dog = 2, elephant = 7

Solve: apple ÷ car + dog = ____?

Answer:

Marks

11) Which letter will complete the words in the sentence? **The SAME letter must fit into BOTH sets of brackets:**

The lea(_) from the tree (_)ell down to the ground.

Answer:

16) **Find the pair of letters and numbers** that will complete the sentence in the best way. The alphabet is provided below to help you:

A B C D E F G H I J K L M N O P Q R S T U V W X Y Z

11JB is to 22LE as 11YM is to ___?

Answer:

12) James only likes certain types of food. Two of them are CARROT and LETTUCE.

Which other two does he like from the following list?

apple, banana, cucumber, peas, orange

Answer:

17) Select the pair of words, one from each group that are opposite in meaning to each other:

The opposite of (ascend, lift, fall) is (escalator, stairs, descend).

Answer:

13) Select the word from the brackets that will complete the sentence in the most sensible way.

Meera said that the test was HARD and DIFFICULT whilst George said it was EASY and (soft, simple, safe)

Answer:

18) Three consecutive letters are removed from the word in CAPITALS. These letters make a word. From the five options below, find the missing letters to complete the sentence:

Joey ate a lot of different MS at the barbecue.

A. OAT
B. EAT
C. ATE
D. ARK
E. END

Answer:

14) Find one word from each group that together makes **one correctly spelt word.** The letters **must not** be rearranged. The word from the first group **must always** be used first:

The (judge, jury, court) (garden, yard, lawn) is a beautiful place to stay!

Answer:

19) Select the TWO odd words from the options given below:

Father, friend, son, mother, neighbour, sister, aunt, uncle

Answer:

15) Find the group of letters that will continue the series. The alphabet is provided below to help you:

A B C D E F G H I J K L M N O P Q R S T U V W X Y Z

MMNN, LLOO, KKPP, JJQQ, IIRR, ___?

Answer:

20) Complete the following functions and sums with the correct numbers and signs as appropriate:

26 − 17 = ___ × 3

A. 3
B. 4
C. 6
D. 7
E. 9

Answer:

Verbal Reasoning

 26

Marks

21) Read the information provided and choose the single best answer for the questions below:

Solve: 5 × ___ = 37 – 12

A. 2
B. 3
C. 5
D. 7
E. 9

Answer:

22) Choose the correct answer for the following problem:

Rajesh has a number. When he divides it by 6 it gives 2 less than 5? What is Rajesh's number?

A. 6
B. 24
C. 12
D. 30
E. 18

Answer:

23) Read the information provided and choose the single best answer for the questions below:

Raparna, James and Payal share 25 bananas so that Raparna has 12 bananas and James has 6 bananas. How many bananas does Payal have?

A. 4
B. 7
C. 9
D. 6
E. 5

Answer:

24) Work out the relationship between the word and the code to solve the code:

A B C D E F G H I J K L M N O P Q R S T U V W X Y Z

You are on a treasure hunt at school and your teacher gave you the following code to solve.

HOUSE = GMROZ.

What is the code for SOFA?

Answer:

25) Read the information provided and choose the single best answer for the question below:

If 10 members of the Spoon and Fork Society committee could decorate the hall in 5 hours, how many committee members would be needed to decorate the hall in 1 hour?

A. 45
B. 60
C. 45
D. 50
E. 55

Answer:

26) The words in brackets are formed from the main word. Identify the pattern to work out the missing word from the 5 options given below:

Begun (gun), saucepan (pan), borrow (?).

A. BOW
B. ROO
C. ROW
D. BROW
E. WOR

Answer:

27) You are required to move one letter from the first word to the second word, creating two new words. This will then complete the sentence.

SPARE BAT

The two fighters were ready to _____ but who would ____ the other?

Answer:

28) Three consecutive letters are removed from the word in CAPITALS. These letters make a word. From the five options below, find the missing letters to complete the sentence:

Payal was paid a lot of MY for her work.

A. ATE
B. EAT
C. ARE
D. ONE
E. OAT

Answer:

29) In each set of numbers, the number in the brackets is related to the two numbers either side of it. Find this relation to work out the missing number '(?)' in the third set. Choose one of the five options below.

6 (9) 3, 14 (16) 2, 7 (?) 4

A. 16
B. 11
C. 5
D. 13
E. 18

Answer:

30) Three consecutive letters have been taken out of a word. Which three letters have been omitted:

The C____PION was defeated in action.

A. HIT
B. HAT
C. HAS
D. HAM
E. BIT

Answer:

www.My11PlusPapers.co.uk

Marks

31) In each set of numbers, the number in the brackets is related to the two numbers either side of it. Find this relation to work out the missing number '(?)' in the third set. Choose one of the five options below.

8 (17) 9, 1 (3) 2, 3 (?) 4

A. 11
B. 12
C. 7
D. 2
E. 25

Answer:

36) Find the group of letters that will continue the series. The alphabet is provided below to help you:

A B C D E F G H I J K L M N O P Q R S T U V W X Y Z

AZ, CB, ED, GF, IH ___?

Answer:

32) A THREE letter word is hidden between two words in the sentence below. These two words are always next to each other, but there may be punctuation between them. Find this four letter word from one of the 5 options.

"It is too far mother," I yelled!

A. far mother
B. It is
C. too far
D. mother I
E. I yelled

Answer:

37) Select the TWO odd words from the options given below:

Plane, helicopter, car, bus, lorry

A. Helicopter car
B. Car bus
C. Lorry plane
D. Plane helicopter
E. Lorry bus

Answer:

33) Find the option that best completes the series. Fill in the missing blank with one of the following five options:

3 plates, 5 forks, 8 plates, 12 forks, ___?

A. 14 plates
B. 19 forks
C. 17 plates
D. 20 plates
E. 21 forks

Answer:

38) The words in brackets are formed from the main word. Identify the pattern to work out the missing word from the 5 options given below:

Bobcat (cat), treadmill (ill), target (?).

A. TAR
B. GILL
C. GET
D. ARE
E. TER

Answer:

34) Select the letter that will complete the word in front of the brackets and begin the word after the brackets. The SAME letter must fit into BOTH sets of brackets:

hai (_) oom, bea (_) ead

Answer:

39) A four letter word is hidden between two words in the sentence below. These two words are always next to each other, but there may be punctuation between them. Find this four letter word from the sentence.

A well-conditioned tuba sells for about £210.

Answer:

35) Select the word from the brackets that will complete the sentence in the most sensible way:

Chocolate is to SWEET as lemon is to (sour, bitter, sweet)

Answer:

40) Choose the correct answer for the following problem:

What number is 6 less than 8 + 50% of 12?

A. 4
B. 7
C. 8
D. 12
E. 14

Answer:

Verbal Reasoning

28

Verbal Reasoning - Test 4

Time allowed for this paper : 60 minutes

Instructions for Best Practice:

> Attempt all of the questions.
> Ensure that your answers are clearly marked in the answer boxes.
> Calculators and rulers must not be used.
> Equipment recommended: 2 x Pencil & 1 x Eraser.

Marks

1) Choose the correct answer for the following problem. Write your answer below:

What number subtracted from sixteen gives an answer that when multiplied by seven gives forty-nine?

A. 9
B. 10
C. 11
D. 12
E. 13

Answer:

2) Read the information provided and choose the single best answer for the question. Write your answer below:

Garage A earned £170 from used car sales. Garage B earned £60 less than Garage A, but double Garage E. Garage D earned £25 more than Garage B, whilst Garage C earned three times the money that Garage E. Which Garage earned the most money?

A. Garage A   D. Garage D
B. Garage B   E. Garage E
C. Garage C

Answer:

3) Three consecutive letters are removed from the word in CAPITALS. From the options, find the missing letters to complete the sentence. Write your answer below:

Driving without a SBELT is very dangerous.

A. EAT
B. EEE
C. TRE
D. CEA
E. AAT

Answer:

4) In each set of numbers, the number in the brackets is related to the two numbers either side of it. Find this relation to work out the missing number '(?)' in the third set. Choose one of the options and write your answer below:

6 (4) 3, 14 (14) 2, 20 (?) 5

A. 8
B. 19
C. 6
D. 14
E. 0

Answer:

5) In each set of numbers, the number in the brackets is related to the two numbers either side of it. Find this relation to work out the missing number '(?)' in the third set. Choose one of the options and write your answer below:

8 (16) 2, 10 (25) 2, 12 (?) 2

A. 14
B. 21
C. 4
D. 2
E. 36

Answer:

6) Read the information provided and choose the single best answer for the question. Write your answer below:

Peter, Lily and Allen walk to the same bus stop every day. Allen arrives 3 minutes later than Peter. If Lily arrives at 7:40 and is one minute earlier than Peter, what time does Allen get to the bus stop?

A. 7:36   D. 7:42
B. 7:38   E. 7:44
C. 7:40

Answer:

7) The words in brackets are formed from the main word. Identify the pattern to work out the missing word from the options given. Write your answer below:

Beating (ate), fearing (are), tethers (?)

A. THE
B. HER
C. SHE
D. SET
E. HET

Answer:

8) A four letter word is hidden between two words in the sentence below. These two words are always next to each other, but there may be punctuation between them. Find this four letter word from one of the options. Write your answer below:

I had a fever yesterday, but today I feel much better.

A. today I   D. much better
B. feel much   E. had a
C. fever yesterday

Answer:

9) A four letter word is hidden between two words in the sentence below. These two words are always next to each other, but there may be punctuation between them. Find this four letter word from one of the options. Write your answer below:

He told me not to look in his handwritten diary but I just could not help myself.

A. handwritten diary
B. look in
C. diary but
D. me not
E. his handwritten

Answer:

10) The words in brackets are formed from the main word. Identify the pattern to work out the missing word from the options given. Write your answer below:

Seating (ate), nearing (are), deserted (?)

A. DET
B. TED
C. SET
D. DER
E. SEE

Answer:

www.My11PlusPapers.co.uk

11) Three consecutive letters are removed from the word in CAPITALS. From the options, find the missing letters to complete the sentence. Write your answer below:

My father could not hear me over the music, so I SHED through the window.

A. MAS
B. STR
C. ECK
D. OUT
E. ANK

Answer:

12) Find the number and word that best completes the series. Fill in the missing blank with one of the following options and write your answer below:

3 sweets, 10 chocolates, ___ , 24 chocolates, 31 sweets

A. 24 chocolates
B. 31 sweets
C. 49 chocolates
D. 17 sweets
E. 12 sweets

Answer:

13) Select the TWO odd words from the options given. Write your answer below:

Talk, Quiet, Speak, Hymn, Whisper.

A. Quiet Speak
B. Whisper Talk
C. Quiet Hymn
D. Whisper Speak
E. Quiet Talk

Answer:

14) Choose the correct answer by completing the following functions and sums with the correct numbers and signs as appropriate. Write your answer below:

$39 \_\_ 13 + 4 \div 2 = 14 + 7 \times 2$

A. +
B. –
C. ×
D. ÷

Answer:

15) Find the pair of letters that will complete the sentence in the best way. The alphabet is provided below to help you. Write your answer below:

A B C D E F G H I J K L M N O P Q R S T U V W X Y Z

PR is to QQ as IK is to ___?

Answer:

16) Select the pair of words, one from each group that are opposite in meaning to each other from the options given below. Write your answer below:

(Take None Student) (Teacher Choose Alight)

A. Take Choose
B. None Alight
C. Student Alight
D. None Choose
E. Student Teacher

Answer:

17) Three consecutive letters have been taken out of a word. Select which three letters have been omitted from the options below:

Carefully ____MERGE the garment in warm water.

A. DUB
B. SUB
C. SIP
D. BAN
E. LIP

Answer:

18) You are required to move one letter from the first word to the second word, creating two new words. Write your answer below:

STOCK RAY

Answer:

19) Work out the relationship between the word and the code to solve the code and write your answer below:

A B C D E F G H I J K L M N O P Q R S T U V W X Y Z

Your teacher organises a treasure hunt for you and your school mates. He gives you the following code to decipher.

AWARD is to DZDUG.

Decode the following: ZDUP.

Answer:

20) Work out the relationship between the word and the code to solve the code and write your answer below:

A B C D E F G H I J K L M N O P Q R S T U V W X Y Z

Your teacher organises a treasure hunt for you and your school mates. He gives you the following code to decipher.

AWARD is to DZDUG.

Decode the following: FRYHU.

Answer:

Marks

21) Using the provided code, complete the following sum writing your answer in <u>letters</u>:

a = 2, b = 16, c = 3, d = 6, e = 4

Solve: c × b ÷ e ÷ a = ___?

Answer:

26) Select the two words **inside the brackets** that are connected in some way to the words **outside the brackets**. Write your answer below:

PEAR BANANA (apple, cabbage, beetroot, bread, orange)

Answer:

22) Write the letter that will **complete the word** in front of the brackets and **begin the word** after the brackets. The SAME letter must fit into BOTH sets of brackets. Write your answer below:

pas (_) ame, nea (_) ake

Answer:

27) Select the word from the brackets that will **complete the sentence** in the most sensible way. Write your answer below:

Sentence is to LETTERS as sum is to (maths, learn, numbers)

Answer:

23) Select the two words **inside the brackets** that are connected in some way to the words **outside the brackets**. Write your answer below:

BOX CRATE (tub, container, carry, store, place)

Answer:

28) Find the pair of letters that will complete the sentence in the best way. The alphabet is provided below to help you. Write your answer below:

A B C D E F G H I J K L M N O P Q R S T U V W X Y Z

TZ is to UX as FL is to ___?

Answer:

24) Using the provided code, complete the following sums writing your answer in <u>code</u>:

grape = 5, orange = 7, apple = 3, coconut = 2, peach = 8

Solve: (orange + peach) ÷ grape = ___?

Answer:

29) Select the pair of words, one from each group that are opposite in meaning to each other from the options given. Write your answer below:

(Success Dedication Hard) (Failure Difficult Novel)

A. Success Failure
B. Success Difficult
C. Hard Difficult
D. Hard Novel
E. Dedication Failure

Answer:

25) Write the letter that will **complete the word** in front of the brackets and **begin the word** after the brackets. The SAME letter must fit into BOTH sets of brackets. Write your answer below:

pai (_) ame, gai (_) eat

Answer:

30) Select the TWO odd words from the options given. Write your answer below:

Cutlery, Spoon, Fork, Knife, Steak.

A. Fork Knife
B. Steak Cutlery
C. Steak Knife
D. Spoon Fork
E. Fork Steak

Answer:

Marks

31) Three consecutive letters have been taken out of a word. Select which three letters have been omitted from the options below:

The BOOK____ was approximately 165 pages long.

A. LIP
B. PUN
C. HER
D. TEN
E. LET

Answer:

36) Choose the correct answer by completing the following functions and sums with the correct numbers and signs as appropriate. Write your answer below:

43 ___ 16 ÷ 8 = 86

A. +
B. −
C. ×
D. ÷

Answer:

32) You are required to move one letter from the first word to the second word, creating two new words. Write your answer below:

SUITE RED.

Answer:

37) Choose the correct answer for the following problem. Write your answer below:

Rob decides to take a bus to get to his meeting which starts at 10:00. The bus journey usually takes 20 minutes but today it takes him twice as long. Given that he got on the bus at 9:35, how late was Rob for his meeting?

A. 5 mins
B. 10 mins
C. 15 mins
D. 20 mins
E. 25 mins

Answer:

33) Select the word from the brackets that will complete the sentence in the most sensible way. Write your answer below:

Speak is to LISTEN as teach is to (work, look, learn)

Answer:

38) Find one word from each group that together make one correctly spelt word. The letters must not be rearranged. The word from the first group must always be used first. Write your answer below:

(sheep, goat, horse) (glove, sock, shoe)

A. Sheepsock
B. Horseshoe
C. Goatglove
D. Horseglove
E. Goatshoe

Answer:

34) Find one word from each group that together make one correctly spelt word. The letters must not be rearranged. The word from the first group must always be used first. Write your answer below:

(hand, head, foot) (path, route, road)

A. Handroute
B. Headpath
C. Footpath
D. Footroad
E. Headroute

Answer:

39) Find the pair of letters that will continue the series. The alphabet is provided below to help you. Write your answer below:

A B C D E F G H I J K L M N O P Q R S T U V W X Y Z

HR, GU, FX, EA, DD, ___?

Answer:

35) Find the pair of letters that will continue the series. The alphabet is provided below to help you. Write your answer below:

A B C D E F G H I J K L M N O P Q R S T U V W X Y Z

RS, SV, TY, UB, VE, ___?

Answer:

40) Find the numbers that best complete the series. Fill in the missing blank with one of the following options and write your answer below:

4, 20, 100, ____, 2,500

A. 300
B. 400
C. 500
D. 800
E. 1,200

Answer:

Verbal Reasoning

33

Verbal Reasoning - Test 5

Time allowed for this paper : 60 minutes

Instructions for Best Practice:

> Attempt all of the questions.
> Ensure that your answers are clearly marked in the answer boxes.
> Calculators and rulers must not be used.
> Equipment recommended: 2 x Pencil & 1 x Eraser.

Marks

1) In each sentence, **three consecutive letters are removed** from the word in CAPITALS. These letters make a word. From the options, find **the missing letters** to complete the sentence. Write your answer below:

Simon hung his CHES out to dry.

A. LIT
B. LOT
C. ART
D. EAR
E. ARE

Answer:

2) In each set of numbers, the number in the brackets is related to **the two numbers either side of it**. Find this relation to work out the missing number '(?)' in the third set. Choose one of the options and write your answer below:

13 (17) 4, 18 (27) 9, 3 (?) 2

A. 5   D. 14
B. 24   E. 9
C. 13

Answer:

3) Find the pair of letters that will continue the series. The alphabet is provided below to help you. Write your answer below:

A B C D E F G H I J K L M N O P Q R S T U V W X Y Z

AZ, DW, GT, JQ, MN, ___?

Answer:

4) Three consecutive letters have been taken out of a word. Select which three letters **have been omitted** from the options below:

The C____NEY was very dusty.

A. HER
B. HAT
C. HIT
D. HAM
E. HIM

Answer:

5) Find the number that **best completes the series**. Fill in the missing blank with one of the following options and write your answer below:

97, 194, 291, 388, ___

A. 485
B. 430
C. 396
D. 512
E. 342

Answer:

6) You are required to **move one letter from the first word to the second word, creating two new words**. These will then complete the sentence.

FILL ACE

I could tell he was not feeling well from his _____ _____.

Answer:

7) Choose the correct answer by **completing the following functions and sums with the correct numbers and signs** as appropriate. Write your answer below:

27 ÷ ___ = 24 − 15

A. 27
B. 9
C. 6
D. 1
E. 3

Answer:

8) You are required to move one letter from the first word to the second word, creating two new words. Write your answer below:

BREAD BEAST

Answer:

9) Choose the correct answer for the following problem. Write your answer below:

Half of a number is 6 less than the product of 4 and 5. What is the number?

A. 34
B. 32
C. 26
D. 28
E. 30

Answer:

10) Work out the relationship between the word and the code to solve the code and write your answer below:

A B C D E F G H I J K L M N O P Q R S T U V W X Y Z

Your teacher organises a treasure hunt for you and your school mates. He gives you the following code to decipher.

HOUSE is to GMROZ.

What is the code for GARDEN?

Answer:

Marks

11) Work out the **relationship** between the word and the code to solve the code and write your answer below:

A B C D E F G H I J K L M N O P Q R S T U V W X Y Z

Your teacher organises a treasure hunt for you and your school mates. He gives you the following code to decipher.

HOUSE is to GMROZ.

Decode the following word CCPG?

Answer:

16) Find the **pair of letters and numbers** that will continue the series. The alphabet is provided below to help you. Write your answer below:

A B C D E F G H I J K L M N O P Q R S T U V W X Y Z

11EM, 22FN , 33GO, 44HP, 55IQ, __?

Answer:

12) Write the letter that will **complete the word** in front of the brackets and begin the word after the brackets. The SAME letter must fit into BOTH sets of brackets. Write your answer below:

hol (_) ark, sai (_) ead

Answer:

17) Find the **pair of letters** that will complete the sentence in the best way. The alphabet is provided below to help you. Write your answer below:

A B C D E F G H I J K L M N O P Q R S T U V W X Y Z

CX is to ___ as FU is to DW?

Answer:

13) Select the two words inside the brackets that are connected in some way to the words outside the brackets. Write your answer below:

HOSPITAL, CHURCH (school, road, station, park, pool)

Answer:

18) Select the pair of words, one from each group that are opposite in meaning to each other from the options given. Write your answer below:

(strong, hospital, healthy) (energetic, medicine, ill)

A. Strong ill
B. Healthy ill
C. Hospital medicine
D. Healthy energetic
E. Strong energetic

Answer:

14) Select the word from the brackets that will complete the sentence in the most sensible way. Write your answer below:

Bed is to SLEEP as chair is to (stand, jump, sit)

Answer:

19) Select the two words **inside the brackets** that are connected in some way to the words **outside the brackets**. Write your answer below:

My favourite animals are SHEEP, GOATS but also (zebras, cows, pigs, lions, bears).

Answer:

15) Find one word **from each group** that together make one correctly spelt word. The letters must not be rearranged. The word from the first group **must always** be used first. Write your answer below:

The (parcel, mail, send) (box, square, cylinder) was outside our house.

A. Sendbox   D. Mailbox
B. Mailsquare   E. Mailcylinder
C. Parcelbox

Answer:

20) Select the pair of words, one from each group that are opposite in meaning to each other from the options given. Write your answer below:

(cocktail, diluted, cordial) (concentrated, watered, drink)

A. Cocktail concentrated
B. Diluted watered
C. Cordial drink
D. Cocktail watered
E. Diluted concentrated

Answer:

Marks

21) Select the TWO odd words from the options given. Write your answer below:

Kitchen, table, stool, sofa, garden, television

- A. Kitchen table
- B. Garden stool
- C. Kitchen garden
- D. Stool sofa
- E. Table sofa

Answer:

22) Choose the correct answer by completing the following functions and sums with the correct numbers and signs as appropriate. Write your answer below:

$41 - 17 = \underline{\quad} \div 2$

- A. 54
- B. 50
- C. 32
- D. 48
- E. 36

Answer:

23) A four letter word is hidden between two words in the sentence below. These two words are always next to each other, but there may be punctuation between them. Find this four letter word from one of the options. Write your answer below:

He bent the tube and the sink suddenly worked!

- A. tube and
- B. and the
- C. sink suddenly
- D. he bent
- E. suddenly worked

Answer:

24) Three consecutive letters have been taken out of a word. Select which three letters have been omitted from the options below:

The sound of a trumpet is quite DIS____CT.

- A. TIN
- B. TAN
- C. TAB
- D. BIN
- E. BAN

Answer:

25) Choose the correct answer for the following problem. Write your answer below:

One fifth of a number plus 12 equals half of 34. What is the number?

- A. 20
- B. 25
- C. 30
- D. 35
- E. 40

Answer:

26) Read the information provided and choose the single best answer for the question. Write your answer below:

Paul, Natasha, Russell, Sarah and Tom go to the theatre and sit side by side.
Paul is not by Russell. Russel sits on the extreme right. Tom sits between Russel and Natasha. Sarah sits next to Paul but not next to Natasha.

Who sits on the extreme left?

- A. Paul
- B. Natasha
- C. Russell
- D. Sarah
- E. Tom

Answer:

27) Read the information provided and choose the single best answer for the question. Write your answer below:

Paul, Natasha, Russell, Sarah and Tom go to the theatre and sit side by side.
Paul is not by Russell. Russel sits on the extreme right. Tom sits between Russel and Natasha. Sarah sits next to Paul but not next to Natasha.

Who sits in the middle?

- A. Paul
- B. Natasha
- C. Russell
- D. Sarah
- E. Tom

Answer:

28) The words in brackets are formed from the main word. Identify the pattern to work out the missing word from the options given. Write your answer below:

Haddock (dock), hotspot (spot), knitwear (?)

- A. WEAR
- B. EAR
- C. TEAR
- D. NEAR
- E. WET

Answer:

29) Select the word from the brackets that will complete the sentence in the most sensible way. Write your answer below:

Doctor is to HOSPITAL as teacher is to (student, books, school)

Answer:

30) The words in brackets are formed from the main word. Identify the pattern to work out the missing word from the options given below. Write your answer below:

Outfit (fit), yourself (elf), robot (?)

- A. BOOT
- B. ROOT
- C. BOT
- D. ROT
- E. ORB

Answer:

Marks

31) Write the letter that will complete the word in front of the brackets and begin the word after the brackets. The SAME letter must fit into BOTH sets of brackets. Write your answer below:

bea (_) not, wea (_) eys

Answer:

32) Three consecutive letters are removed from the word in CAPITALS. These letters make a word. From the five options below, find the missing letters to complete the sentence. Write your answer below:

Dr Patel MED the exam papers.

A. ATE
B. EAR
C. ARC
D. ART
E. ARK

Answer:

33) In each set of numbers, the number in the brackets is related to the two numbers either side of it. Find this relation to work out the missing number '(?)' in the third set. Choose one of the five options below.

10 (17) 7, 3 (7) 4, 19 (?) 21

A. 17   D. 12
B. 5   E. 40
C. 25

Answer:

34) A four letter word is hidden between two words in the sentence below. These two words are always next to each other, but there may be punctuation between them. Find this four letter word from one of the options. Write your answer below:

The Globe still shows some of Shakespeare's works from the 1600s.

A. some of   D. globe still
B. shows some   E. from the
C. works from

Answer:

35) Find the numbers that best complete the series. Fill in the missing blank with one of the following options and write your answer below:

258, 369, 480, 591, ___

A. 599
B. 604
C. 638
D. 692
E. 702

Answer:

36) Using the provided code, complete the following sums writing your answer in numbers:

apple = 8, ball = 0, car = 4, desk = 2, egg = 7.

Solve: desk × car × ball = ___?

Answer:

37) Using the provided code, complete the following sums writing your answer in numbers:

apple = 8, ball = 0, car = 4, desk = 2, egg = 7.

Solve: apple – car × desk + ball = ___?

Answer:

38) Find the pair of letters that will complete the sentence in the best way. The alphabet is provided below to help you. Write your answer below:

A B C D E F G H I J K L M N O P Q R S T U V W X Y Z

QE is to SG as UL is to ___?

Answer:

39) Find one word from each group that together makes one correctly spelt word. The letters must not be rearranged. The word from the first group must always be used first. Write your answer below:

I left my (magazine, leaflet, book) (pen, mark, page) in the library.

A. Bookmark
B. Magazinepen
C. Leafletmark
D. Bookpage
E. Magazinepage

Answer:

40) Select the TWO odd words from the options given. Write your answer below:

Bread, pasta, juice, pancake, coffee

A. Bread pasta
B. Juice pasta
C. Juice coffee
D. Bread pancake
E. Coffee pancake

Answer:

www.My11PlusPapers.co.uk

Verbal Reasoning - Test 6

Time allowed for this paper : 60 minutes

Instructions for Best Practice:

> Attempt all of the questions.
> Ensure that your answers are clearly marked in the answer boxes.
> Calculators and rulers must not be used.
> Equipment recommended: 2 x Pencil & 1 x Eraser.

Verbal Reasoning - Test 6

1) Three consecutive letters are removed from the word in CAPITALS. These letters make a word. From the options, Find the missing letters to complete the sentence. Write your answer below:

Riddhi commented that the LIGHG in the room was poor.

A. TAP
B. TAN
C. TEN
D. TIP
E. TIN

Answer:

2) Write the letter that will complete the word in front of the brackets and begin the word after the brackets. The SAME letter must fit into BOTH sets of brackets. Write your answer below:

bea (_) ude, kee (_) ice

Answer:

3) Find the numbers that best complete the series. Fill in the missing blank with one of the following options and write your answer below:

15 cars, 19 cars, 23 cars, 27 cars, ___ cars.

A. 29
B. 31
C. 32
D. 28
E. 30

Answer:

4) Three consecutive letters have been taken out of a word. Select which three letters have been omitted from the options. Write your answer below:

The dart hit the BULLS___!

A. EAR
B. EAT
C. EYE
D. END
E. CAT

Answer:

5) You are required to move one letter from the first word to the second word, creating two new words. These will then complete the sentence.

CAST CAR

The poor _____ had a large _____ across its face.

Answer:

6) Find the pair of letters that will continue the series. The alphabet is provided below to help you. Write your answer below:

A B C D E F G H I J K L M N O P Q R S T U V W X Y Z

AA, BC, CE, DG, EI, ___?

Answer:

7) Work out the relationship between the word and the code to solve the code and write your answer below:

A B C D E F G H I J K L M N O P Q R S T U V W X Y Z

HOUSE is to GMROZ. Decode the following: BFXEM.

Answer:

8) Using the provided code, complete the following sums writing your answer in numbers:

apple = 2, ball = 9, chair = 7, desk = 3, egg = 5.

Solve: ball ÷ desk =___?

Answer:

9) Using the provided code, complete the following sums writing your answer in numbers:

apple = 2, ball = 9, chair = 7, desk = 3, egg = 5.

Solve: egg + apple = ___?

Answer:

10) Write the letter that will complete the word in front of the brackets and begin the word after the brackets. The SAME letter must fit into BOTH sets of brackets. Write your answer below:

slo (_) alk, sho (_) ish

Answer:

40

www.My11PlusPapers.co.uk

Marks

11) Select the two words **inside the brackets** that are connected in some way to the words **outside the brackets**. Write your answer below:

SEA, POOL (park, lake, river, court, pavement)

Answer:

16) Find one word **from each group** that together makes **one correctly spelt word**. The letters must not be rearranged. The word from the first group **must always be used first**. Write your answer below:

"(moon, planet, star) (dirt, dust, powder) is a magical substance!" exclaimed Mrs Patel!

A. Planetdust
B. Stardust
C. Moonpowder
D. Stardirt
E. Moondirt

Answer:

12) **Work out the relationship** between the word and the code to solve the code and write your answer below:

A B C D E F G H I J K L M N O P Q R S T U V W X Y Z

HOUSE is to GMROZ. Decode the following: JGQYCYG

Answer:

17) Find the pair of letters that will continue the series. The alphabet is provided below to help you. Write your answer below:

A B C D E F G H I J K L M N O P Q R S T U V W X Y Z

RT, VX, ZB, DF, HJ, ___?

Answer:

13) Select the two words **inside the brackets** that are connected in some way to the words **outside the brackets**. Write your answer below:

DAFFODIL ROSE (tree, apple, tulip, sunflower, pear)

Answer:

18) A four letter word is hidden between two words in the sentence below. These two words are always next to each other, but there may be punctuation between them. Find this **four letter word** from one of the options. Write your answer below:

Not being able to solve the Rubik's cube started to make her very agitated.

A. being able   D. started to
B. cube started   E. very agitated
C. make her

Answer:

14) Select the word from the brackets that will complete the sentence in the most sensible way. Write your answer below:

Baker is to BREAD as butcher is to (candles, meat, shop)

Answer:

19) Find the pair of letters that will complete the sentence in the best way. The alphabet is provided below to help you. Write your answer below:

A B C D E F G H I J K L M N O P Q R S T U V W X Y Z

SK is to QN as VE is to ___?

Answer:

15) Find one word **from each group** that together make **one correctly spelt word**. The letters **must not be rearranged**. The word from the first group **must always be used first**. Write your answer below:

The young boy wrote in his (note, message, type) (book, letter, novel).

A. messagebook   D. notebook
B. typenovel   E. typebook
C. noteletter

Answer:

20) Find the pair of letters that will complete the sentence in the best way. The alphabet is provided below to help you. Write your answer below:

A B C D E F G H I J K L M N O P Q R S T U V W X Y Z

NP is to OO as GI is to ___?

Answer:

www.My11PlusPapers.co.uk

Marks

21) Select the word from the brackets that will complete the sentence in the most sensible way. Write your answer below:

Father is to SON as mother is to (daughter, brother, baby)

Answer:

22) Select the pair of words, one from each group that are **opposite in meaning** to each other from the options given below. Write your answer below:

The opposite of (lazy, kind, thoughtless) is (generous, cruel, dishonest).

A. Lazy generous
B. Thoughtless dishonest
C. Kind cruel
D. Kind dishonest
E. Lazy cruel

Answer:

23) Select the **TWO odd words** from the options given. Write your answer below:

Judo, tennis, hockey, swimming, cricket

A. Judo swimming
B. Swimming cricket
C. Cricket hockey
D. Hockey judo
E. Hockey tennis

Answer:

24) Choose the correct answer by **completing the following functions and sums** with the **correct numbers and signs** as appropriate. Write your answer below:

2 + 2 = 64 ÷ __

A. 4
B. 8
C. 16
D. 32
E. 64

Answer:

25) The words in brackets are formed from the main word. Identify the pattern to work out the **missing word** from the options given. Write your answer below:

Shape (ape), stink (ink), nausea (?)

A. NEA
B. SEA
C. USEA
D. ASEA
E. ANE

Answer:

26) Choose the correct answer by **completing the following functions and sums** with the **correct numbers and signs** as appropriate. Write your answer below:

2 + 4 + __ = 19 − 7

A. 3
B. 6
C. 9
D. 12
E. 14

Answer:

27) Choose the correct answer for the following problem. Write your answer below:

When a third of 21 is added to a certain number you get 13. What is the number?

A. 5
B. 6
C. 7
D. 8
E. 9

Answer:

28) Select the pair of words, one from each group that are **opposite in meaning** to each other from the options given. Write your answer below:

The opposite of (wide, vague, long) is (motorway, broad, narrow).

A. Wide broad
B. Vague narrow
C. Long motorway
D. Wide narrow
E. Long narrow

Answer:

29) Choose the correct answer for the following problem. Write your answer below:

One quarter of a number subtracted from 20 equals 13, what is the number?

A. 16
B. 20
C. 24
D. 28
E. 32

Answer:

30) Read the information provided and choose the single best answer for the question. Write your answer below:

There are 4 shops on the street. One is painted purple, one green, one blue and one white.
The purple and blue shops are large while the green and white shops are small. The purple and green shops sell sweets while the blue and white shops sell stationary.

What colour is the large stationary shop?

A. Purple
B. Green
C. Blue
D. White
E. Yellow

Answer:

www.My11PlusPapers.co.uk

Marks

31) Read the information provided and choose the single best answer for the question. Write your answer below:

There are 4 shops on the street. One is painted purple, one green, one blue and one white.
The purple and blue shops are large while the green and white shops are small. The purple and green shops sell sweets while the blue and white shops sell stationary.

What colour is the small sweet shop?

A. Purple   D. White
B. Green   E. Yellow
C. Blue

Answer:

32) The words in brackets are formed from the main word. Identify the pattern to work out the missing word from the options given. Write your answer below:

Kitchen (hen), copycat (cat), watchdog (?)

A. DOG
B. HOG
C. WATCH
D. DAG
E. WOG

Answer:

33) Select the TWO odd words from the options given. Write your answer below:

Stomach, clothes, liver, body, brain

A. Clothes body
B. Clothes brain
C. Stomach liver
D. Liver body
E. Body brain

Answer:

34) Three consecutive letters are removed from the word in CAPITALS. These letters make a word. From the options, find the missing letters to complete the sentence. Write your answer below:

Emma had to REHSE for the show.

A. EAR
B. EAT
C. BAR
D. CAR
E. ATE

Answer:

35) In each set of numbers, the number in the brackets is related to the two numbers either side of it. Find this relation to work out the missing number '(?)' in the third set. Choose one of the options and write your answer below:

13 (15) 2, 1 (5) 6, 8 (?) 7

A. 16
B. 10
C. 2
D. 12
E. 15

Answer:

36) You are required to move one letter from the first word to the second word, creating two new words. Write your answer below:

BEAN RED

Answer:

37) In each set of numbers, the number in the brackets is related to the two numbers either side of it. Find this relation to work out the missing number '(?)' in the third set. Choose one of the option and write your answer below:

12 (15) 3, 17 (19) 2, 7 (?) 1

A. 18   D. 13
B. 6   E. 8
C. 11

Answer:

38) A four letter word is hidden between two words in the sentence below. These two words are always next to each other, but there may be punctuation between them. Find this four letter word from one of the options. Write your answer below:

He had a very interesting hobby: he was a robe enthusiast!

A. hobby he
B. robe enthusiast
C. interesting hobby
D. a robe
E. very interesting

Answer:

39) Find the numbers that best complete the series. Fill in the missing blank with one of the following options and write your answer below:

6, 14, 30, 54, ___

A. 44
B. 83
C. 32
D. 86
E. 73

Answer:

40) Three consecutive letters have been taken out of a word. Select which three letters have been omitted from the options. Write your answer below:

The small ___GER buried himself in the bushes.

A. DAD
B. HAD
C. BAT
D. BAD
E. HAT

Answer:

Verbal Reasoning - Test 7

Time allowed for this paper : 60 minutes

Instructions for Best Practice:

> Attempt all of the questions.
> Ensure that your answers are clearly marked in the answer boxes.
> Calculators and rulers must not be used.
> Equipment recommended: 2 x Pencil & 1 x Eraser.

1) Using the provided code, complete the following sums writing your answer in numbers:

ants = 2, bees = 9, crickets = 7, dogs = 3, elephants = 5

Solve: bees ÷ dogs – ants =

Answer:

2) Using the provided code, complete the following sums writing your answer in numbers:

ants = 2, bees = 9, crickets = 7, dogs = 3, elephants = 5

Solve: crickets – dogs x ants =

Answer:

3) In each set of numbers, the number in the brackets is related to the two numbers either side of it. Find this relation to work out the missing number '(?)' in the third set. Choose one of the option and write your answer below:

1 (8) 7, 4 (12) 8, 7 (?) 9

A. 2
B. 19
C. 16
D. 3
E. 17

Answer:

4) Read the information provided and choose the single best answer for the question. Write your answer below:

ANDY, BETH, CARL, DAVID and EMMA are walking individually in the park.
Emma is EAST of Carl. Carl in turn is EAST of Beth.

Carl is NORTH of David and SOUTH of Andy.

Question: Who is the furthest WEST?

A. Andy   D. David
B. Beth   E. Emma
C. Carl

Answer:

5) Read the information provided and choose the single best answer for the question. Write your answer below:

ANDY, BETH, CARL, DAVID and EMMA are walking individually in the park.
Emma is EAST of Carl. Carl in turn is EAST of Beth.

Carl is NORTH of David and SOUTH of Andy.

Question: Who is the furthest NORTH?

A. Andy   D. David
B. Beth   E. Emma
C. Carl

Answer:

6) A four letter word is hidden between two words in the sentence below. These **two words are always next to each other**, but there may be punctuation between them. Find this **four letter word** from one of the options. Write your answer below:

The tall gazebo attracted many unfamiliar faces into our garden.

A. tall gazebo
B. unfamiliar faces
C. attracted many
D. gazebo attracted
E. our garden

Answer:

7) Choose the correct answer for the following problem. Write your answer below:

If twenty-four is six less than two times this number, what is the number?

A. 13
B. 14
C. 15
D. 16
E. 17

Answer:

8) The words in brackets are formed from the main word. Identify the pattern to work out the missing word from the options given. Write your answer below:

Prepare (are), furiously (sly), diplomat (?)

A. MAT
B. DIT
C. LIP
D. LAT
E. PAT

Answer:

9) Three consecutive letters are removed from the word in CAPITALS. These letters make a word.
From the options, find the missing letters to complete the sentence. Write your answer below:

Bob threw away the BISH in the bin.

A. RAN
B. RUN
C. RUB
D. RUT
E. RAT

Answer:

10) In each set of numbers, the number in the brackets is related to the two numbers either side of it. Find this relation to work out the missing number '(?)' in the third set. Choose one of the options and write your answer below:

14 (20) 6, 9 (13) 4, 10 (?) 3

A. 13
B. 6
C. 18
D. 22
E. 3

Answer:

Verbal Reasoning

45

Marks

11) A four letter word is hidden between two words in the sentence below. These **two words are always next to each other**, but there **may be punctuation between them**. Find this **four letter word** from one of the options. Write your answer below:

The gazebo needed to be put up correctly.

A. the gazebo
B. put up
C. gazebo needed
D. up correctly
E. needed to

Answer:

16) Select the two words **inside the brackets** that are connected in some way to the words **outside the brackets**. Write your answer below:

DOG CAT (parrot, hamster, tiger, wolf, elephant)

Answer:

12) Find the numbers that best complete the series. Fill in the missing blank with one of the following options and write your answer below:

3 peas, 10 peas, 17 peas, 24 peas, ___ peas?

A. 21
B. 29
C. 34
D. 36
E. 31

Answer:

17) Find one word from each group that together makes one correctly spelt word. The letters must not be rearranged. The word from the first group must always be used first. Write your answer below:

Ali asked the waitress for a (coffee, tea, water) (pan, mug, pot).

A. Waterpot
B. Coffeemug
C. Teapot
D. Teapan
E. Waterpan

Answer:

13) Three consecutive letters have been taken out of a word. Select which three letters **have been omitted** from the options. Write your answer below:

The monarch reclined on his THR____.

A. ONE
B. TWO
C. SIX
D. ANT
E. ARM

Answer:

18) Find the pair of letters that will continue the series. The alphabet is provided below to help you. Write your answer below:

A B C D E F G H I J K L M N O P Q R S T U V W X Y Z

WV, VU, TS, QP, ML, ___?

Answer:

14) Work out the relationship between the word and the code to solve the code and write your answer below:

A B C D E F G H I J K L M N O P Q R S T U V W X Y Z

TEMPLE is to RCKNJC. What is the code for CHURCH?

Answer:

19) Find the pair of letters that will complete the sentence in the best way. The alphabet is provided below to help you. Write your answer below:

A B C D E F G H I J K L M N O P Q R S T U V W X Y Z

CW is to EY as KZ is to ___?

Answer:

15) Work out the relationship between the word and the code to solve the code and write your answer below:

A B C D E F G H I J K L M N O P Q R S T U V W X Y Z

TEMPLE is to RCKNJC. What is the code for PALACE?

Answer:

20) Select the pair of words, one from each group that are **opposite in meaning** to each other from the options given below. Write your answer below:

The opposite of (hot, coffee, cup) is (milk, mug, cold).

A. Hot cold
B. Coffee cold
C. Cup milk
D. Hot milk
E. Cup mug

Answer:

www.My11PlusPapers.co.uk

Marks

21) Choose the correct answer by completing the following functions and sums with the correct numbers and signs as appropriate. Write your answer below:

7 – ___ = 3 – (4 – 2)

A. 6
B. 4
C. 1
D. 2
E. 3

Answer:

26) Select the word from the brackets that will complete the sentence in the most sensible way. Write your answer below:

Hard is to FIRM as weak is to (frail, day, strong)

Answer:

22) Three consecutive letters are removed from the word in CAPITALS. These letters make a word. From the options, find the missing letters to complete the sentence. Write your answer below:

Kisan turned on the fan as the TEMPEURE was too hot.

A. RAT
B. RAN
C. CAT
D. CAN
E. CAR

Answer:

27) Three consecutive letters have been taken out of a word. Select which three letters have been omitted from the options. Write your answer below:

The toddler fell down and got a SC___CH on his knee.

A. RUN
B. RAM
C. RAN
D. RIP
E. RAT

Answer:

23) Find the number that best completes the series. Fill in the missing blank with one of the following options and write your answer below:

27, 36, 45, 54, ___

A. 63
B. 72
C. 59
D. 58
E. 65

Answer:

28) You are required to move one letter from the first word to the second word, creating two new words. These can then complete the sentence.

STATUE FOND

The 3 _____s of matter that have been _____ are solid, liquid and gas.

Answer:

24) Select the TWO odd words from the options given. Write your answer below:

Flute, viola, clarinet, trumpet, drum

A. Flute clarinet
B. Viola drum
C. Drum trumpet
D. Trumpet viola
E. Trumpet flute

Answer:

29) Select the two words inside the brackets that are connected in some way to the words outside the brackets. Write your answer below:

CRICKET SPIDER (ant, cat, beetle, parrot, dog)

Answer:

25) Find the pair of letters that will complete the sentence in the best way. The alphabet is provided below to help you. Write your answer below:

A B C D E F G H I J K L M N O P Q R S T U V W X Y Z

SM is to TK as NF is to ___?

Answer:

30) Select the word from the brackets that will complete the sentence in the most sensible way. Write your answer below:

Happy is to SAD as strong is to (hard, firm, weak)

Answer:

Marks

31) Select the pair of words, one from each group that are opposite in meaning to each other from the options given. Write your answer below:

(halt, broad, cheap) (stop, wide, expensive)

A. Halt stop
B. Broad wide
C. Cheap wide
D. Cheap expensive
E. Broad stop

Answer:

36) Choose the correct answer by completing the following functions and sums with the correct numbers and signs as appropriate. Write your answer below:

$(2 \times 4) \div (\_\_ - 6) = 8$

A. 6
B. 7
C. 8
D. 9
E. 10

Answer:

32) Select the TWO odd words from the options given. Write your answer below:

Triangle, drum, xylophone, violin, trombone

A. Violin xylophone
B. Xylophone drum
C. Drum trombone
D. Triangle trombone
E. Violin trombone

Answer:

37) You are required to move one letter from the first word to the second word, creating two new words. Write your answer below:

TIME ASK

Answer:

33) Choose the correct answer for the following problem. Write your answer below:

If eight is two more than one-third of this number, what is this number?

A. 18
B. 21
C. 24
D. 27
E. 30

Answer:

38) Write the letter that will complete the word in front of the brackets and begin the word after the brackets. The SAME letter must fit into BOTH sets of brackets. Write your answer below:

wal (_) eak, mal (_) ife

Answer:

34) The words in brackets are formed from the main word. Identify the pattern to work out the missing word from the options given. Write your answer below:

Sewage (wage), stubborn (born), riverbank (?)

A. BANK
B. RANK
C. ANK
D. EANK
E. RINK

Answer:

39) Find one word from each group that together makes one correctly spelt word. The letters must not be rearranged. The word from the first group must always be used first. Write your answer below:

Sam always wanted a (gold, grey, bronze) (frog, fish, monkey) as a pet.

A. Greyfish
B. Goldmonkey
C. Goldfish
D. Bronzefrog
E. Bronzemonkey

Answer:

35) Find the pair of letters that will continue the series. The alphabet is provided below to help you. Write your answer below:

A B C D E F G H I J K L M N O P Q R S T U V W X Y Z

IC, HD, GE, FF, EG, __?

Answer:

40) Write the letter that will complete the word in front of the brackets and begin the word after the brackets. The SAME letter must fit into BOTH sets of brackets. Write your answer below:

nai (_) ast, tal (_) ies

Answer:

www.My11PlusPapers.co.uk

Verbal Reasoning - Test 8

Time allowed for this paper : 60 minutes

Instructions for Best Practice:

> Attempt all of the questions.
> Ensure that your answers are clearly marked in the answer boxes.
> Calculators and rulers must not be used.
> Equipment recommended: 2 x Pencil & 1 x Eraser.

Marks

1) Read the information provided and choose the single best answer for the question. Write your answer below:

ANDY, BETH, CARL, DAVID and EMMA are walking individually in the park.
Emma is EAST of Carl. Carl in turn is EAST of Beth.
Carl is NORTH of David and SOUTH of Andy.

Who is the furthest EAST?

Answer:

A. Andy   D. David
B. Beth   E. Emma
C. Carl

2) Read the information provided and choose the single best answer for the question. Write your answer below:

ANDY, BETH, CARL, DAVID and EMMA are walking individually in the park.
Emma is EAST of Carl. Carl in turn is EAST of Beth.
Carl is NORTH of David and SOUTH of Andy.

Who is the furthest SOUTH?

Answer:

A. Andy   D. David
B. Beth   E. Emma
C. Carl

3) Find the number that best completes the series. Fill in the missing blank with one of the following options and write your answer below:

12 carrots, 7 carrots, 13 carrots, 9 carrots, 14 carrots, ___ carrots?

A. 15
B. 17
C. 9
D. 11
E. 10

Answer:

4) In each set of numbers, the number in the brackets is related to the two numbers either side of it. Find this relation to work out the missing number '(?)' in the third set. Choose one of the option and write your answer below:

4 (4) 0, 19 (21) 2, 13 (?) 4

A. 13   D. 7
B. 17   E. 15
C. 16

Answer:

5) Choose the correct answer for the following problem. Write your answer below:

If thirty-two is four less than six times this number, what is the number?

A. 2
B. 3
C. 4
D. 5
E. 6

Answer:

6) The words in brackets are formed from the main word. Identify the pattern to work out the missing word from the options given. Write your answer below:

Recall (call), sawdust (dust), hyperlink (?)

A. RINK
B. PINK
C. LINK
D. HINK
E. YINK

Answer:

7) Select the pair of words, one from each group that are opposite in meaning to each other from the options given. Write your answer below:

The opposite of (request, accept, tell) is (ask, shout, refuse).

A. Request refuse
B. Accept refuse
C. Tell ask
D. Tell shout
E. Accept shout

Answer:

8) Select the TWO odd words from the options given. Write your answer below:

French, Spanish, India, Hindi, Germany, Latin

A. India Germany
B. Hindi French
C. Spanish Germany
D. India Hindi
E. French Spanish

Answer:

9) Find one word from each group that together makes one correctly spelt word. The letters must not be rearranged. The word from the first group must always be used first. Write your answer below:

He kicked the (foot, finger, toe) (bat, racket, ball) across the park.

A. Fingerball
B. Toebat
C. Footracket
D. Fingerbat
E. Football

Answer:

10) Find the pair of letters that will continue the series. The alphabet is provided below to help you. Write your answer below:

A B C D E F G H I J K L M N O P Q R S T U V W X Y Z

DR, ES, GU, JX, NB, ___?

Answer:

Verbal Reasoning

50

Marks

11) Work out the relationship **between the word** and the code to solve the code and write your answer below:

A B C D E F G H I J K L M N O P Q R S T U V W X Y Z

You are at an ancient relic in Peru. You notice a code inscribed on the wall.

TEMPLE is to RCKNJC.

What is the code for HOUSE?

Answer:

12) Work out the **relationship** between the word and the code to solve the code and write your answer below:

A B C D E F G H I J K L M N O P Q R S T U V W X Y Z

You are at an ancient relic in Peru. You notice a code inscribed on the wall.

TEMPLE is to RCKNJC.

Decode the following: YJRCP

Answer:

13) Write the letter that will complete the word in front of the brackets and begin the word after the brackets. The SAME letter must fit into BOTH sets of brackets. Write your answer below:

han (_) umb, min (_) amp

Answer:

14) Select the two words **inside the brackets** that are connected in some way to the words **outside the brackets**. Write your answer below:

WATER JUICE (cheese, milk, yoghurt, lemonade, bread)

Answer:

15) Write the letter that will complete the word in front of the brackets and **begin the word after the brackets**. The SAME letter must fit into BOTH sets of brackets. Write your answer below:

mis (_) eal, til (_) ile

Answer:

16) Find one word **from each group** that together makes one correctly spelt word. The letters must not be rearranged. The word from the first group must always be used first. Write your answer below:

Maddy sunk her teeth into the moist (mug, cup, glass) (cake, cookie, bread).

A. Mugcake
B. Cupcookie
C. Glassbread
D. Mugbread
E. Cupcake

Answer:

17) Find the pair of letters and numbers that will complete the sentence in the best way. The alphabet is provided below to help you. Write your answer below:

A B C D E F G H I J K L M N O P Q R S T U V W X Y Z

T11V is to R33X as M11O is to ___?

Answer:

18) Select the pair of words, one from each group that are opposite in meaning to each other from the options given below. Write your answer below:

The opposite of (rude, considerate, good) is (polite, thoughtful, helpful)

A. Considerate polite
B. Rude polite
C. Good helpful
D. Rude helpful
E. Good thoughtful

Answer:

19) Choose the correct answer for the following problem. Write your answer below:

If sixteen is five less than three times this number, what is the number?

A. 3
B. 5
C. 7
D. 9
E. 11

Answer:

20) The words in brackets are formed from the main word. Identify the pattern to work out the missing word from the options given. Write your answer below:

Quicksand (sand), detour (tour), sidewalk (?)

A. DEAL
B. WALK
C. DALK
D. SEAL
E. LADS

Answer:

www.My11PlusPapers.co.uk

Marks

21) Choose the correct answer by **completing the following functions and sums** with the **correct numbers and signs** as appropriate. Write your answer below:

(7 + 6 + 4) × ___ = 34

A. 8
B. 2
C. 9
D. 7
E. 4

Answer:

22) **Find the pair of letters** that will complete the sentence in the best way. The alphabet is provided below to help you. Write your answer below:

A B C D E F G H I J K L M N O P Q R S T U V W X Y Z

AM is to YK as DS is to ___?

Answer:

23) Select the **TWO odd words** from the options given. Write your answer below:

River, sand, sea, lake, forest, ocean

A. River sand
B. Sea forest
C. Sea lake
D. Sand forest
E. Lake river

Answer:

24) Choose the correct answer by **completing the following functions and sums** with the **correct numbers and signs** as appropriate. Write your answer below:

(7 × ___) − (6 × 2) = 16

A. 1
B. 3
C. 5
D. 2
E. 4

Answer:

25) **Three consecutive letters** have been taken out of a word. Select which three letters **have been omitted** from the options. Write your answer below:

The actor carefully read his SC___T.

A. RUN
B. RAM
C. RAN
D. RIP
E. RAT

Answer:

26) You are required to **move one letter from the first word to the second word**, creating two new words. Write your answer below:

BUST PAN

Answer:

27) **Using the provided code**, complete the following sums writing your answer in numbers:

apple = 2, ball = 9, carrot = 7, dog = 3, egg = 5.

Solve: carrot + egg − apple × dog = ___?

Answer:

28) Select the two words **inside the brackets** that are connected in some way to the words **outside the brackets**. Write your answer below:

James only likes to read from a BOOK, BROCHURE, (game, magazine, phone, newspaper, television)

Answer:

29) Select the word from the brackets that will complete the sentence in the most sensible way. Write your answer below:

Car is to ROAD as train is to (track, station, engine)

Answer:

30) **Using the provided code**, complete the following sums writing your answer in numbers:

a = 10, b = 4, c = 0, d = 3, e = 9.

Solve: a × c = ___?

Answer:

Verbal Reasoning

52

31) Select the word from the brackets that will complete the sentence in the most sensible way. Write your answer below:

Water is to DRINK as bread is to (smell, watch, eat)

Answer:

36) A four letter word is hidden between two words in the sentences below. These **two words are always next to each other**, but there may be punctuation between them. Find this **four letter word** from one of the options. Write your answer below:

Can you please set up the gazebo? Sure, no problem it will be done!

A. set up
B. the gazebo
C. sure no
D. no problem
E. problem it

Answer:

32) Three consecutive letters are removed from the word in CAPITALS. These letters make a word. From the options, find the missing letters to complete the sentence. Write your answer below:

Harmanda took a VAION in Peru.

A. BAT
B. CAT
C. CAR
D. MAT
E. EAR

Answer:

37) A four letter word is hidden between two words in the sentence below. These **two words are always next to each other**, but there may be punctuation between them. Find this **four letter word** from one of the options. Write your answer below:

I entered my neighbour's gazebo thinking I could get some free food.

A. entered my
B. thinking I
C. could get
D. gazebo thinking
E. some free

Answer:

33) Find the pair of letters and numbers that will continue the series. The alphabet is provided below to help you. Write your answer below:

A B C D E F G H I J K L M N O P Q R S T U V W X Y Z

1F2G, 3H4I, 5J6K, 7L8M, 9N10O, ___?

Answer:

38) Find the numbers that best complete the series. Fill in the missing blank with one of the following options and write your answer below:

9, 15, 10, 16, ___

A. 13
B. 18
C. 11
D. 17
E. 14

Answer:

34) Three consecutive letters have been taken out of a word. Select which three letters **have been omitted** from the options. Write your answer below:

We need to DISTR____ the guard if we are to escape.

A. ANT
B. ACT
C. ARM
D. ARC
E. OWN

Answer:

39) You are required to move one letter from the first word to the second word, creating two new words. Write your answer below:

CRAMP SEA

Answer:

35) In each set of numbers, the number in the brackets is related to the two numbers either side of it. Find this relation to work out the missing number '(?)' in the third set. Choose one of the options and write your answer below:

3 (8) 5, 1 (4) 3, 2 (?) 4

A. 10   D. 4
B. 24   E. 6
C. 7

Answer:

40) Three consecutive letters are removed from the word in CAPITALS. These letters make a word. From the options, find the missing letters to complete the sentence. Write your answer below:

Russell ate some GES with his lunch.

A. RAN
B. CAP
C. CAT
D. RAP
E. CAN

Answer:

Secondary
Entrance

Verbal Reasoning - Test 9

Time allowed for this paper : 60 minutes

Instructions for Best Practice:

> Attempt all of the questions.
> Ensure that your answers are clearly marked in the answer boxes.
> Calculators and rulers must not be used.
> Equipment recommended: 2 x Pencil & 1 x Eraser.

Marks

1) Work out the relationship between the word and the code to solve the code and write your answer below:

A B C D E F G H I J K L M N O P Q R S T U V W X Y Z

You are at an ancient relic in Peru. You notice a code inscribed on the wall.

TEMPLE is to RCKNJC.

Decode the following: NPGCQR.

Answer:

2) Work out the relationship between the word and the code to solve the code and write your answer below:

A B C D E F G H I J K L M N O P Q R S T U V W X Y Z

You are at an ancient relic in Peru. You notice a code inscribed on the wall.

TEMPLE is to RCKNJC.

Decode the following: UYRCP.

Answer:

3) Select the word from the brackets that will complete the sentence in the most sensible way. Write your answer below:

Light is to HEAVY as dark is to (light, dim, night)

Answer:

4) Find one word from each group that together makes one correctly spelt word. The letters must not be rearranged. The word from the first group must always be used first. Write your answer below:

It was a beautiful Sunday (before, during, after) (day, noon, night).

A. Afternoon
B. Afterday
C. Beforenight
D. Duringnoon
E. Beforeday

Answer:

5) Choose the correct answer for the following problem. Write your answer below:

Two times 15 is the same as a number multiplied by six, what is the number?

A. 5
B. 7
C. 8
D. 3
E. 6

Answer:

6) Read the information provided and choose the single best answer for the question. Write your answer below:

2 boys, KABIR and SHIV, and 2 girls, ROSHNI and RIDDHI, are four children who each take part in three of the following 4 sports: hockey, tennis, swimming, volleyball. Only Riddhi does not play volleyball. Shiv and Riddhi are the only children who swim.
Kabir, Roshni and Riddhi play hockey.

Which girl can swim?

A. Kabir
B. Shiv
C. Roshni
D. Riddhi
E. None

Answer:

7) Read the information provided and choose the single best answer for the question. Write your answer below:

2 boys, KABIR and SHIV, and 2 girls, ROSHNI and RIDDHI, are four children who each take part in three of the following 4 sports: hockey, tennis, swimming, volleyball. Only Riddhi does not play volleyball. Shiv and Riddhi are the only children who swim.
Kabir, Roshni and Riddhi play hockey.
Which boy plays volleyball but can't swim?

A. Kabir
B. Shiv
C. Roshni
D. Riddhi
E. None

Answer:

8) The words in brackets are formed from the main word. Identify the pattern to work out the missing word from the options given. Write your answer below:

Screenplay (play), depart (part), overheat (?)

A. EAT
B. HEAT
C. ATE
D. RATE
E. HOT

Answer:

9) Three consecutive letters are removed from the word in CAPITALS. These letters make a word. From the options, find the missing letters to complete the sentence. Write your answer below:

Shiv had CUSD with his apple pie.

A. TAN
B. TAR
C. TAB
D. CAR
E. CAB

Answer:

10) Choose the correct answer for the following problem. Write your answer below:

If thirteen is three more than double this number, what is the number?

A. 2
B. 3
C. 4
D. 5
E. 6

Answer:

Marks

11) The words in brackets are formed from the main word. Identify the pattern to work out the **missing word** from the options given. Write your answer below:

Crosswind (wind), midweek (week), eyewash (?)

A. YASH
B. HEYE
C. WASH
D. WESH
E. YESH

Answer:

12) In each set of numbers, the number in the brackets is related to **the two numbers either side of it**. Find this relation to work out the missing number '(?)' in the third set. Choose one of the option and write your answer below:

16 (30) 14, 13 (19) 6, 17 (?) 14

A. 11   D. 31
B. 28   E. 9
C. 16

Answer:

13) A four letter word is hidden between two words in the sentence below. These two words are always next to each other, but there may be punctuation between them. Find this four letter word from one of the options. Write your answer below:

This replica means a lot to me, perhaps even more than the original.

A. perhaps even   D. replica means
B. than the   E. even more
C. means a

Answer:

14) A four letter word is hidden between two words in the sentence below. These two words are always next to each other, but there may be punctuation between them. Find this four letter word from one of the options. Write your answer below:

Veronica met with the headmaster to discuss her failing grades.

A. headmaster to   D. veronica met
B. with the   E. discuss her
C. failing grades

Answer:

15) Find the number that best completes the series. Fill in the missing blank with one of the following options and write your answer below:

84 bricks, 86 shovels, 90 bricks, 92 shovels, 96 bricks, ___ ?

A. 100 bricks
B. 102 shovels
C. 98 shovels
D. 104 shovels
E. 97 bricks

Answer:

16) Select the pair of words, one from each group that are opposite in meaning to each other from the options given. Write your answer below:

The opposite of (asleep, close, fall) is (awake, plan, dream).

A. Asleep awake
B. Asleep dream
C. Fall awake
D. Close plan
E. Close dream

Answer:

17) Select the **TWO** odd words from the options given. Write your answer below:

Dutch, Belgium, Asia, Austria, Italy

A. Belgium Dutch
B. Asia Austria
C. Dutch Asia
D. Italy Austria
E. Belgium Italy

Answer:

18) Find the pair of letters that will complete the sentence in the best way. The alphabet is provided below to help you. Write your answer below:

A B C D E F G H I J K L M N O P Q R S T U V W X Y Z

PO is to RP as HG is to ___?

Answer:

19) Select the word from the brackets that will complete the sentence in the most sensible way. Write your answer below:

Happy is to ELATED as sad is to (happiness, miserable, envious)

Answer:

20) Find one word from each group that together makes one correctly spelt word. The letters must not be rearranged. The word from the first group **must always be used first.** Write your answer below:

As morning broke, (day, dusk, morning) (lamp, light, bulb) gleemed through the curtains.

A. Morninglight
B. Duskbulb
C. Daylamp
D. Daylight
E. Dusklamp

Answer:

Marks

21) Using the provided code, complete the following sums writing your answer in numbers:

apple = 10, ball = 4, carrot = 0, dog = 3, egg = 9

Solve: egg – ball = ___?

Answer:

22) Using the provided code, complete the following sums writing your answer in numbers:

ants = 10, beetle = 4, cricket = 0, dog = 3, elephant = 9

Solve: ants – elephant ÷ dog = ___?

Answer:

23) Write the letter that will complete the word in front of the brackets and begin the word after the brackets. The SAME letter must fit into BOTH sets of brackets. Write your answer below:

han (_) ong, gan (_) one

Answer:

24) Select the two words inside the brackets that are connected in some way to the words outside the brackets. Write your answer below:

Janice only likes certain types of animals. She likes the PARROT, OSTRICH (budgie, monkey, pigeon, hare, badger)

Answer:

25) Find the pair of letters that will continue the series. The alphabet is provided below to help you. Write your answer below:

A B C D E F G H I J K L M N O P Q R S T U V W X Y Z

NO, MP, LQ, KR, JS, ___?

Answer:

26) Choose the correct answer by completing the following functions and sums with the **correct numbers and signs** as appropriate. Write your answer below:

155 – 11 = 12 × ___

A. 9
B. 10
C. 11
D. 12
E. 13

Answer:

27) Three consecutive letters are removed from the word in CAPITALS. These letters make a word. From the options, find the missing letters to complete the sentence. Write your answer below:

Julie went to the MET to buy some bread.

A. AND
B. END
C. ARK
D. ACE
E. ART

Answer:

28) In each set of numbers, the number in the brackets is related to the two numbers either side of it. Find this relation to work out the missing number '(?)' in the third set. Choose one of the options and write your answer below:

12 (20) 8, 18 (19) 1, 23 (?) 15

A. 30   D. 19
B. 10   E. 38
C. 21

Answer:

29) Find the pair of letters that will complete the sentence in the best way. The alphabet is provided below to help you. Write your answer below:

A B C D E F G H I J K L M N O P Q R S T U V W X Y Z

LB is to NA as MR is to ___?

Answer:

30) Select the pair of words, one from each group that are opposite in meaning to each other from the options given below. Write your answer below:

The opposite of (many, some, all) is (end, complete, few).

A. Many complete
B. Some end
C. Some few
D. All complete
E. Many few

Answer:

www.My11PlusPapers.co.uk

Marks

31) Three consecutive letters have been taken out of a word. Select which three letters **have been omitted** from the options. Write your answer below:

The was a DISTUR___CE in the neighbourhood.

A. BAT
B. BUN
C. BAN
D. CAT
E. CAN

Answer:

36) Choose the correct answer by **completing the following functions and sums** with the correct numbers and signs as appropriate. Write your answer below:

20 − 8 = __ ÷ 4

A. 36
B. 44
C. 28
D. 32
E. 48

Answer:

32) You are required to move one letter from the first word to the second word, creating two new words. Write your answer below:

TRUST PAIN

Answer:

37) Find the number that best completes the series. Fill in the missing blank with one of the following options and write your answer below:

3, 9, 15, 21, ___?

A. 30
B. 33
C. 35
D. 27
E. 31

Answer:

33) Three consecutive letters have been taken out of a word. Select which three letters have been omitted from the options. Write your answer below:

The man was hypnotised, as if he was in a T___CE.

A. RAN
B. RUN
C. RIP
D. RAM
E. RAP

Answer:

38) You are required to move one letter from the first word to the second word, creating two new words. Write your answer below:

BOAT MAT

Answer:

34) Find the pair of letters that will continue the series. The alphabet is provided below to help you. Write your answer below:

A B C D E F G H I J K L M N O P Q R S T U V W X Y Z

JL, NP, RT, VX, ZB, ___?

Answer:

39) Write the letter that will complete the word in front of the brackets and begin the word after the brackets. The SAME letter must fit into BOTH sets of brackets. Write your answer below:

lim (_) ick, dam (_) ump

Answer:

35) Select the TWO odd words from the options given. Write your answer below:

Jeans, hand, neck, coat, jumper, trouser

A. Hand coat
B. Jeans jumper
C. Jumper coat
D. Hand neck
E. Neck coat

Answer:

40) Select the two words inside the brackets that are connected in some way to the words outside the brackets. Write your answer below:

Ronny only likes certain types of animals. He likes the LION, TIGER, (wolf, fox, cheetah, panther, antelope)

Answer:

Verbal Reasoning - Test 10

Time allowed for this paper : 60 minutes

Instructions for Best Practice:

> Attempt all of the questions.
> Ensure that your answers are clearly marked in the answer boxes.
> Calculators and rulers must not be used.
> Equipment recommended: 2 x Pencil & 1 x Eraser.

Secondary Entrance

Marks

1) Work out the relationship **between the word** and the code to solve the code and write your answer below:

A B C D E F G H I J K L M N O P Q R S T U V W X Y Z

Your teacher gives you the following code to decipher as part of your homework.

PLAY is to OMZZ.

What is the code for TOY?

Answer:

2) Work out the relationship **between the word** and the code to solve the code and write your answer below:

A B C D E F G H I J K L M N O P Q R S T U V W X Y Z

PLAY is to OMZZ. What is the code for STORY?

Answer:

3) Find one word from each group that together makes one correctly spelt word. The letters must not be rearranged. The word from the first group **must always** be used first. Write your answer below:

She always dreamed of singing in the (space, area, spot) (bright, light, dark).

A. Spacelight   D. Spotlight
B. Areadark   E. Spacedark
C. Spotbright

Answer:

4) Find the pair of letters that will continue the series. The alphabet is provided below to help you. Write your answer below:

A B C D E F G H I J K L M N O P Q R S T U V W X Y Z

TS, RQ, PO, NM, LK, __?

Answer:

5) Select the pair of words, one from each group that are **opposite in meaning** to each other from the options given. Write your answer below:

The opposite of (medicine, remedy, healthy) is (sick, cure, doctor).

A. Medicine sick
B. Remedy cure
C. Healthy sick
D. Healthy doctor
E. Medicine cure

Answer:

6) Select the TWO odd words from the options given. Write your answer below:

Soap, shower gel, bath, shampoo, clean

A. Soap bath
B. Shower gel clean
C. Soap shampoo
D. Bath shampoo
E. Bath clean

Answer:

7) Read the information provided and choose the single best answer for the question. Write your answer below:

2 boys, KABIR and SHIV, and 2 girls, ROSHNI and RIDDHI, are four children who each take part in three of the following 4 sports: hockey, tennis, swimming, volleyball Only Riddhi does not play volleyball. Shiv and Riddhi are the only children who swim.
Kabir, Roshni and Riddhi play hockey.

What sport does everyone take part in?

A. Hockey   D. Volleyball
B. Tennis   E. None
C. Swimming

Answer:

8) Read the information provided and choose the single best answer for the question. Write your answer below:

2 boys, KABIR and SHIV, and 2 girls, ROSHNI and RIDDHI, are four children who each take part in three of the following 4 sports: hockey, tennis, swimming, volleyball Only Riddhi does not play volleyball. Shiv and Riddhi are the only children who swim.
Kabir, Roshni and Riddhi play hockey.

What sport does Shiv not play?

A. Hockey   D. Volleyball
B. Tennis   E. None
C. Swimming

Answer:

9) Find the numbers that best complete the series. Fill in the missing blank with one of the following options and write your answer below:

30, 27, 23, 18, 12, ___

A. 5
B. 11
C. 8
D. 10
E. 9

Answer:

10) Three consecutive letters are removed from the word in CAPITALS. These letters make a word. From the options, find the missing letters to complete the sentence. Write your answer below:

Beth FED the jug with water.

A. ARK
B. AND
C. ALE
D. END
E. ILL

Answer:

11) In each set of numbers, the number in the brackets is related to **the two numbers either side of it.** Find this relation to work out the missing number '(?)' in the third set. Choose one of the options and write your answer below:

18 (24) 6, 14 (21) 7, 8 (?) 15

A. 14   D. 23
B. 9   E. 1
C. 15

Answer:

16) **Find the pair of letters** that will complete the sentence in the best way. The alphabet is provided below to help you. Write your answer below:

A B C D E F G H I J K L M N O P Q R S T U V W X Y Z

JK is to LN as CD is to ___?

Answer:

Marks

12) Write the letter that will complete the word in front of the brackets and begin the word after the brackets. The SAME letter must fit into BOTH sets of brackets. Write your answer below:

sca (_) ift, pea (_) ear

Answer:

17) Select the pair of words, one from each group that are opposite in meaning to each other from the options given below. Write your answer below:

(flowing, tide, river) (wave, stagnant, sea)

A. Tide wave
B. River sea
C. Flowing stagnant
D. Tide sea
E. River stagnant

Answer:

13) Select the two words inside the brackets that are connected in some way to the words outside the brackets. Write your answer below:

SPHERE CYLINDER (triangle, pentagon, square, cuboid, pyramid)

Answer:

18) Three consecutive letters are removed from the word in CAPITALS. These letters make a word. From the options, find the missing letters to complete the sentence. Write your answer below:

Ragul was the MANR of the company.

A. AGE
B. ATE
C. EAT
D. EAR
E. ARE

Answer:

14) Select the word from the brackets that will **complete the** sentence in the most sensible way. Write your answer below:

Purple is to COLOUR as square is to (size, box, shape)

Answer:

19) In each set of numbers, the number in the brackets is related to **the two numbers either side of it.** Find this relation to work out the missing number '(?)' in the third set. Choose one of the option and write your answer below:

31 (34) 3, 8 (13) 5, 3 (?) 24

A. 32   D. 15
B. 27   E. 2
C. 7

Answer:

15) Find one word **from each group** that together makes one correctly spelt word. The letters **must not be rearranged.** The word from the first group **must always be used first.** Write your answer below:

The actors got themselves ready because it was (show, stage, sound) (time, day, minute).

A. Soundday   D. Stagetime
B. Showtime   E. Soundminute
C. Showday

Answer:

20) A four letter word is hidden between two words in the sentence below. These **two words are always next to each other,** but there may be punctuation between them. Find this four letter word from one of the options. Write your answer below:

This basilica really is as beautiful as they say.

A. really is   D. basilica really
B. as they   E. they say
C. as beautiful

Answer:

Secondary Entrance

Marks

21) A four letter word is hidden between two words in each sentence below. These two words are always next to each other, but there may be punctuation between them. Find this four letter word from one of the options. Write your answer below:

Monica seemed fine, even though she hurt herself playing tennis.

A. monica seemed
B. seemed fine
C. hurt herself
D. though she
E. herself playing

Answer:

26) Write the letter that will complete the word in front of the brackets and begin the word after the brackets. The SAME letter must fit into BOTH sets of brackets. Write your answer below:

pin (_) ick, tal (_) ite

Answer:

22) Choose the correct answer for the following problem. Write your answer below:

What number is three times half of 6 multiplied by two?

A. 21
B. 18
C. 15
D. 24
E. 27

Answer:

27) Select the two words inside the brackets that are connected in some way to the words outside the brackets. Write your answer below:

DOCTOR FIREMAN (brother, teacher, baker, friend, mother)

Answer:

23) The words in brackets are formed from the main word. Identify the pattern to work out the missing word from the options given. Write your answer below:

Forgive (give), predefine (fine), spellbind (?)

A. LINS
B. BIND
C. BINS
D. BINE
E. PIND

Answer:

28) Find the pair of letters that will complete the sentence in the best way. The alphabet is provided below to help you. Write your answer below:

A B C D E F G H I J K L M N O P Q R S T U V W X Y Z

EY is to BA as GQ is to ___?

Answer:

24) Three consecutive letters have been taken out of a word. Select which three letters have been omitted from the options. Write your answer below:

The ___CHER was open on a Sunday morning.

A. KIT
B. BAN
C. BAT
D. BUN
E. BUT

Answer:

29) Select the TWO odd words from the options given. Write your answer below:

Silk, jacket, leather, nylon, iron, cotton

A. Silk nylon
B. Jacket iron
C. Iron leather
D. Silk leather
E. Leather jacket

Answer:

25) You are required to move one letter from the first word to the second word, creating two new words. Write your answer below:

WARD ATE

Answer:

30) Choose the correct answer by completing the following functions and sums with the correct numbers and signs as appropriate. Write your answer below:

___ + 19 = 45

A. 22
B. 24
C. 26
D. 28
E. 30

Answer:

Verbal Reasoning

62

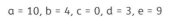
Marks

31) Using the provided code, complete the following sums writing your answer in numbers:

a = 10, b = 4, c = 0, d = 3, e = 9

Solve: e ÷ d × b = ___?

Answer:

36) Choose the correct answer for the following problem. Write your answer below:

An orange and 2 apples costs 86p. 2 oranges and 2 apples cost £1.16. How much is an apple?

A. 23p
B. 25p
C. 24p
D. 28p
E. 26p

Answer:

32) Using the provided code, complete the following sums writing your answer in numbers:

a = 10, b = 4, c = 0, d = 3, e = 9

Solve: a − b + e ÷ d = ___?

Answer:

37) The words in brackets are formed from the main word. Identify the pattern to work out the missing word from the options given. Write your answer below:

Pothole (hole), sapphire (hire), female (?)

A. FALE
B. EEL
C. MALE
D. ALE
E. LAFE

Answer:

33) Select the word from the brackets that will complete the sentence in the most sensible way. Write your answer below:

Night is to DARK as day is to (light, sun, sky)

Answer:

38) Find the number that best completes the series. Fill in the missing blank with one of the following options and write your answer below:

22 jewels, 28 jewels, 35 jewels, 43 jewels, 52 jewels, ___ jewels?

A. 62
B. 68
C. 58
D. 54
E. 61

Answer:

34) Find the pair of letters that will continue the series. The alphabet is provided below to help you. Write your answer below:

A B C D E F G H I J K L M N O P Q R S T U V W X Y Z

CV, DW, EX, FY, GZ, ___?

Answer:

39) Three consecutive letters have been taken out of a word. Select which three letters have been omitted from the options. Write your answer below:

Beware, there are many T____S around the ancient temple.

A. RAP
B. RAN
C. RAT
D. BAT
E. BAN

Answer:

35) Choose the correct answer by completing the following functions and sums with the correct numbers and signs as appropriate. Write your answer below:

396 = ___ + 7

A. 363
B. 377
C. 385
D. 389
E. 379

Answer:

40) You are required to move one letter from the first word to the second word, creating two new words that will complete the sentence. Write your answer below:

WARM DON

After putting his ____ up to answer a question, he finally put it _____.

Answer:

Verbal Reasoning - Test 11

Time allowed for this paper : 60 minutes

Instructions for Best Practice:

> Attempt all of the questions.
> Ensure that your answers are clearly marked in the answer boxes.
> Calculators and rulers must not be used.
> Equipment recommended: 2 x Pencil & 1 x Eraser.

Verbal Reasoning - Test 11

1) Three consecutive letters have been taken out of a word. Select which three letters have been omitted from the options below:

John cleared his THR____ and continued to speak.

A. BAT
B. OAT
C. CAT
D. ATE
E. URN

Answer:

2) You are required to move one letter from the first word to the second word, creating two new words. Write your answer below:

SPIT ACE.

Answer:

3) Work out the relationship between the word and the code to solve the code and write your answer below:

A B C D E F G H I J K L M N O P Q R S T U V W X Y Z

Your teacher organises a treasure hunt for you and your school mates. He gives you the following code to decipher.

PLAY is to OMZZ.

What is the code for SHOW?

Answer:

4) Work out the relationship between the word and the code to solve the code and write your answer below:

A B C D E F G H I J K L M N O P Q R S T U V W X Y Z

Your teacher organises a treasure hunt for you and your school mates. He gives you the following code to decipher.

PLAY is to OMZZ.

Decode the following: APNL

Answer:

5) Find the pair of letters that will continue the series. The alphabet is provided below to help you. Write your answer below:

A B C D E F G H I J K L M N O P Q R S T U V W X Y Z

EH, GJ, JM, NQ, SV, ___?

Answer:

6) Find the pair of letters that will complete the sentence in the best way. The alphabet is provided below to help you. Write your answer below:

A B C D E F G H I J K L M N O P Q R S T U V W X Y Z

ON is to PM as TS is to __?

Answer:

7) Choose the correct answer by completing the following functions and sums with the correct numbers and signs as appropriate. Write your answer below:

12 x ___ = 6 x 124

A. 38
B. 44
C. 58
D. 60
E. 62

Answer:

8) Choose the correct answer for the following problem. Write your answer below:

What is the difference between six times nine and eight multiplied by five?

A. 14
B. 22
C. 16
D. 12
E. 13

Answer:

9) The words in brackets are formed from the main word. Identify the pattern to work out the missing word from the options given. Write your answer below:

Navigate (gate), withdraw (draw), headgear (?)

A. HEAR
B. EAR
C. GEAR
D. DEAR
E. ARE

Answer:

10) Three consecutive letters are removed from the word in CAPITALS. These letters make a word. From the options, find the missing letters to complete the sentence. Write your answer below:

Nathan had to RET the homework.

A. PAT
B. PAN
C. PAW
D. PEN
E. PEA

Answer:

www.My11PlusPapers.co.uk

Marks

11) A four letter word is hidden between two words in the sentence below. These two words are always next to each other, but there may be punctuation between them. Find this four letter word from one of the options. Write your answer below:

Be careful not to fall over, the ground is quite slippery.

A. careful not
B. the ground
C. fall over
D. is quite
E. quite slippery

Answer:

16) Using the provided code, complete the following sums writing your answer in numbers:

a = 1, b = 12, c = 9, d = 5, e = 4

Solve: c + e − d = __?

Answer:

12) A four letter word is hidden between two words in the sentence below. These two words are always next to each other, but there may be punctuation between them. Find this four letter word from one of the options. Write your answer below:

This mountain side is quite steep; it is amazing how some climbers make it right to the top.

A. mountain side
B. right to
C. quite steep
D. amazing how
E. climbers make

Answer:

17) Using the provided code, complete the following sums writing your answer in numbers:

& = 1, £ = 12, $ = 9, @ = 5, € = 4

Solve: & x £ − @ = __?

Answer:

13) Find the number and letter that best completes the series. Fill in the missing blank with one of the following options and write your answer below:

41X, 34Y, 27X, 20Y, ___

A. 10X
B. 14Y
C. 12X
D. 18Y
E. 13X

Answer:

18) Write the letter that will complete the word in front of the brackets and begin the word after the brackets. The SAME letter must fit into BOTH sets of brackets. Write your answer below:

com (_) ike, sta (_) its

Answer:

14) Find the pair of letters that will complete the sentence in the best way. The alphabet is provided below to help you. Write your answer below:

A B C D E F G H I J K L M N O P Q R S T U V W X Y Z

MP is to NO as YB is to __?

Answer:

19) Write the letter that will complete the word in front of the brackets and begin the word after the brackets. The SAME letter must fit into BOTH sets of brackets. Write your answer below:

sof (_) xis, dat (_) rea

Answer:

15) Select the pair of words, one from each group that are opposite in meaning to each other from the options given below. Write your answer below:

(hot, warm, coat) (cold, ice, fan)

A. Warm cold
B. Warm ice
C. Coat fan
D. Hot cold
E. Hot ice

Answer:

20) Select the two words inside the brackets that are connected in some way to the words outside the brackets. Write your answer below:

BREAD CAKE (cheese, biscuit, pastry, salad, fruit)

Answer:

www.My11PlusPapers.co.uk

Marks

21) Select the pair of words, one from each group that are opposite in meaning to each other from the options given. Write your answer below:

(snow, freeze, ice) (sun, hot, heat)

A. Snow sun
B. Freeze heat
C. Ice hot
D. Snow heat
E. Ice sun

Answer:

26) In each set of numbers, the number in the brackets is related to the two numbers either side of it. Find this relation to work out the missing number '(?)' in the third set. Choose one of the option and write your answer below:

8 (2) 6, 7 (5) 2, 11 (?) 3

A. 6
B. 8
C. 16
D. 1
E. 14

Answer:

22) Select the TWO odd words from the options given. Write your answer below:

Violin, guitar, tuba, tambourine, cello

A. Tuba tambourine
B. Guitar tuba
C. Violin cello
D. Cello tambourine
E. Violin tuba

Answer:

27) Find the number that best completes the series. Fill in the missing blank with one of the following options and write your answer below:

332, 279, 226, 173, ___

A. 122
B. 132
C. 120
D. 102
E. 109

Answer:

23) Read the information provided and choose the single best answer for the question. Write your answer below:

In a group of 5 children, Mary is not as old as Simon or Kush but is older than Sharon and Adam. Sharon is not the youngest and Kush is not the oldest.

Who is the oldest?

A. Mary   D. Sharon
B. Simon   E. Adam
C. Kush

Answer:

28) Find the pair of letters that will continue the series. The alphabet is provided below to help you. Write your answer below:

A B C D E F G H I J K L M N O P Q R S T U V W X Y Z

MP, KR, IT, GV, EX, ___?

Answer:

24) Read the information provided and choose the single best answer for the question. Write your answer below:

In a group of 5 children, Mary is not as old as Simon or Kush but is older than Sharon and Adam. Sharon is not the youngest and Kush is not the oldest.

Who is the youngest?

A. Mary   D. Sharon
B. Simon   E. Adam
C. Kush

Answer:

29) Select the TWO odd words from the options given. Write your answer below:

Spend, dollar, pound, cent, exchange

A. Dollar pound
B. Pound cent
C. Spend exchange
D. Spend dollar
E. Exchange pound

Answer:

25) The words in brackets are formed from the main word. Identify the pattern to work out the missing word from the options given. Write your answer below:

Tornadoes (does), breakfast (fast), define (?)

A. FINE
B. FIN
C. DEN
D. DINE
E. DIE

Answer:

30) Choose the correct answer by completing the following functions and sums with the correct numbers and signs as appropriate. Write your answer below:

5 × 45 = (5 × ___) + 30

A. 39
B. 22
C. 18
D. 26
E. 31

Answer:

Marks

31) Choose the correct answer for the following problem. Write your answer below:

I get a total of 30 when I add half of 18 to a third of a certain number. What is that number?

A. 57
B. 63
C. 60
D. 54
E. 51

Answer:

36) Three consecutive letters have been taken out of a word. Select which three letters have been omitted from the options below:

C____R

A. ACT
B. ART
C. ARE
D. ANE
E. ASK

Answer:

32) Select the word from the brackets that will complete the sentence in the most sensible way. Write your answer below:

Square is to CUBE as circle is to (cylinder, pyramid, sphere)

Answer:

37) You are required to move one letter from the first word to the second word, creating two new words. Write your answer below:

MOVIE SAD

Answer:

33) Find one word from each group that together makes one correctly spelt word. The letters must not be rearranged. The word from the first group must always be used first. Write your answer below:

(snow, hail, rain) (bow, tie, hat)

A. Hailbow
B. Rainbow
C. Snowhat
D. Rainhat
E. Snowtie

Answer:

38) Select the word from the brackets that will complete the sentence in the most sensible way. Write your answer below:

Plane is to FLY as bus is to (wheel, drive, road)

Answer:

34) Three consecutive letters are removed from the word in CAPITALS. These letters make a word. From the options, find the missing letters to complete the sentence. Write your answer below:

Kabir ESED from being caught.

A. COP
B. CAP
C. COD
D. COT
E. CAN

Answer:

39) Find one word from each group that together makes one correctly spelt word. The letters must not be rearranged. The word from the first group must always be used first. Write your answer below:

(bath, sink, shower) (room, house, garden)

A. Showerroom
B. Sinkhouse
C. Bathgarden
D. Showerhouse
E. Bathroom

Answer:

35) In each set of numbers, the number in the brackets is related to the two numbers either side of it. Find this relation to work out the missing number '(?)' in the third set. Choose one of the options and write your answer below:

10 (6) 4, 15 (9) 6, 11 (?) 7

A. 4
B. 9
C. 15
D. 14
E. 16

Answer:

40) Select the two words inside the brackets that are connected in some way to the words outside the brackets. Write your answer below:

CHEESE MILK (cake, ice-cream, yoghurt, cereal, biscuit)

Answer:

www.My11PlusPapers.co.uk

Verbal Reasoning - Test 12

Time allowed for this paper : 60 minutes

Instructions for Best Practice:

> Attempt all of the questions.
> Ensure that your answers are clearly marked in the answer boxes.
> Calculators and rulers must not be used.
> Equipment recommended: 2 x Pencil & 1 x Eraser.

Marks

1) Three consecutive letters have been taken out of a word. Select which three letters have been omitted from the options below:

She placed her valuables in a small C____ET.

A. ARM
B. ART
C. APP
D. ANT
E. ASK

Answer:

2) You are required to move one letter from the first word to the second word, creating two new words. Write your answer below:

FAST PEAR.

Answer:

3) Find one word from each group that together makes one correctly spelt word. The letters must not be rearranged. The word from the first group must always be used first. Write your answer below:

(flash, bright, loud) (light, lamp, torch)

A. Brightlight
B. Flashtorch
C. Flashlight
D. Loudlamp
E. Brightlamp

Answer:

4) Find the pair of letters that will continue the series. The alphabet is provided below to help you. Write your answer below:

A B C D E F G H I J K L M N O P Q R S T U V W X Y Z

YW, XV, WU, VT, ___?

Answer:

5) Select the pair of words, one from each group that are opposite in meaning to each other from the options given. Write your answer below:

(send, letter, post) (offer, receive, box)

A. Send offer
B. Post box
C. Send receive
D. Post receive
E. Letter receive

Answer:

6) Select the TWO odd words from the options given. Write your answer below:

Hammer, build, table, spanner, saw

A. Hammer build
B. Build table
C. Saw table
D. Spanner hammer
E. Saw spanner

Answer:

7) Read the information provided and choose the single best answer for the question. Write your answer below:

In a group of 5 children, Mary is not as old as Simon or Kush but is older than Sharon and Adam. Sharon is not the youngest and Kush is not the oldest.

Who is the middle child in terms of age?

A. Mary   D. Sharon
B. Simon   E. Adam
C. Kush

Answer:

8) In each sentence, three consecutive letters are removed from the word in CAPITALS. These letters make a word. From the options, find the missing letters to complete the sentence. Write your answer below:

Aparna wanted to SD time with Annie.

A. PAN
B. PEA
C. PEN
D. PAW
E. PET

Answer:

9) In each set of numbers, the number in the brackets is related to the two numbers either side of it. Find this relation to work out the missing number '(?)' in the third set. Choose one of the options and write your answer below:

11 (2) 9, 15 (7) 8, 19 (?) 7

A. 22
B. 11
C. 9
D. 17
E. 12

Answer:

10) In each set of numbers, the number in the brackets is related to the two numbers either side of it. Find this relation to work out the missing number '(?)' in the third set. Choose one of the option and write your answer below:

9 (4) 5, 12 (3) 9, 8 (?) 7

A. 13
B. 5
C. 1
D. 10
E. 24

Answer:

Marks

---

11) Find the number that best completes the series. Fill in the missing blank with one of the following options and write your answer below:

33, 32, 29, 24, 17, __

A. 13
B. 11
C. 10
D. 6
E. 8

Answer:

---

12) Using the provided code, complete the following sums writing your answer in numbers:

a = 1, b = 12, c = 9, d = 5, e = 4

Solve: (b − e) × a =__?

Answer:

---

13) Using the provided code, complete the following sums writing your answer in numbers:

a = 1, b = 12, c = 9, d = 5, e = 4

Solve: c × b + a =__?

Answer:

---

14) Write the letter that will complete the word in front of the brackets and begin the word after the brackets. The SAME letter must fit into BOTH sets of brackets. Write your answer below:

las (_) arp, mas (_) ilt

Answer:

---

15) Select the two words inside the brackets that are connected in some way to the words outside the brackets. Write your answer below:

BEE WASP (spider, worm, butterfly, moth, caterpillar)

Answer:

---

16) Select the word from the brackets that will complete the sentence in the most sensible way. Write your answer below:

Arm is to LEG as hand is to (foot, toe, finger)

Answer:

---

17) Find the pair of letters that will complete the sentence in the best way. The alphabet is provided below to help you. Write your answer below:

A B C D E F G H I J K L M N O P Q R S T U V W X Y Z

DI is to FF as NS is to __?

Answer:

---

18) Select the TWO odd words from the options given. Write your answer below:

Plate, dinner, tea, teapot, cup

A. Tea teapot
B. Cup tea
C. Plate dinner
D. Teapot plate
E. Dinner tea

Answer:

---

19) Choose the correct answer to complete the following functions and sums with the correct numbers and signs as appropriate. Write your answer below:

39 × 16 = __ + (39 × 15)

A. 41
B. 39
C. 37
D. 44
E. 54

Answer:

---

20) Read the information provided and choose the single best answer for the question. Write your answer below:

Xinyu is facing South-West. She then turns 270°clockwise, 90° anti-clockwise and finally 270° clockwise.

What direction is she now facing?

A. North-East
B. South-West
C. North-West
D. North
E. West

Answer:

---

www.My11PlusPapers.co.uk

Marks

21) The words in brackets are formed from the main word. Identify the pattern to work out the **missing word** from the options given. Write your answer below:

Behalf (half), snowflake (lake), heartless (?)

A. HEAR
B. TEAR
C. TESS
D. ART
E. LESS

Answer:

22) A four letter word is hidden between two words in the sentence below. These **two words are always next to each other**, but there may be punctuation between them. Find this **four letter word** from one of the options. Write your answer below:

Question:
To make it all the way to the top, you must work hard.

A. it all
B. must work
C. the top
D. make it
E. work hard

Answer:

23) A four letter word is hidden between two words in the sentence below. These **two words are always next to each other**, but there may be punctuation between them. Find this **four letter word** from one of the options. Write your answer below:

If there is a will, there is a way.

A. there is
B. a will
C. will there
D. if there
E. a way

Answer:

24) Write the letter that will **complete the word in front of the brackets** and begin the word after the brackets. The SAME letter must fit into BOTH sets of brackets. Write your answer below:

har (_) ast, wor (_) ilk

Answer:

25) Select the two words **inside the brackets** that are connected in some way to the words **outside the brackets**. Write your answer below:

CAR BIKE (park, scooter, motorbike, helmet, road)

Answer:

26) Work out the relationship **between the word and the code** to solve the code and write your answer below:

A B C D E F G H I J K L M N O P Q R S T U V W X Y Z

PLAY is to OMZZ. Decode the following: ZDSPQ

Answer:

27) Work out the relationship **between the word and the code** to solve the code and write your answer below:

A B C D E F G H I J K L M N O P Q R S T U V W X Y Z

PLAY is to OMZZ. Decode the following: FSNVME.

Answer:

28) Find one word from each group that together makes **one correctly spelt word**. The letters must **not be rearranged**. The word from the first group must **always** be used first. Write your answer below:

(rain, snow, hail) (flake, fleck, scale)

A. Snowflake
B. Rainscale
C. Hailflake
D. Snowfleck
E. Hailscale

Answer:

29) Find the pair of letters that will continue the series. The alphabet is provided below to help you. Write your answer below:

A B C D E F G H I J K L M N O P Q R S T U V W X Y Z

AZ, EV, IR, MN, QJ, ___?

Answer:

30) Three consecutive letters have been taken out of a word. Select which three letters have been omitted from the options below:

C_____PER

A. HAT
B. HIT
C. HUT
D. HOP
E. HOT

Answer:

Marks

31) You are required to move one letter from the first word to the second word, creating two new words. Write your answer below:

PAIR EACH

Answer:

32) Select the word from the brackets that will complete the sentence in the most sensible way. Write your answer below:

Eye is to SEE as nose is to (smell, taste, feel)

Answer:

33) Find the pair of letters that will complete the sentence in the best way. The alphabet is provided below to help you. Write your answer below:

A B C D E F G H I J K L M N O P Q R S T U V W X Y Z

CA is to DF as KM is to ___?

Answer:

34) Select the pair of words, one from each group that are opposite in meaning to each other from the options given below. Write your answer below:

(dawn, day, morning) (night, noon, daybreak)

A. Day noon
B. Dawn noon
C. Morning daybreak
D. Day daybreak
E. Day night

Answer:

35) Choose the correct answer to complete the following functions and sums with the correct numbers and signs as appropriate. Write your answer below:

39 ÷ ___ = 12 − 9

A. 3
B. 6
C. 9
D. 12
E. 13

Answer:

36) The words in brackets are formed from the main word. Identify the pattern to work out the missing word from the options given. Write your answer below:

Heirless (less), padlock (lock), baking (?)

A. BIN
B. BING
C. KING
D. BAN
E. KIN

Answer:

37) Three consecutive letters are removed from the word in CAPITALS. These letters make a word. From the options, find the missing letters to complete the sentence. Write your answer below:

Dan rode in the LE car up the mountain.

A. DAB
B. CAB
C. CAT
D. CAR
E. BAR

Answer:

38) Find the numbers that best complete the series. Fill in the missing blank with one of the following options and write your answer below:

31, 9, 29, 8, 27, ___

A. 7
B. 16
C. 25
D. 5
E. 19

Answer:

39) Choose the correct answer for the following problem. Write your answer below:

If I add eight to a certain number, I get an answer which is 7 less than 32. What is the number?

A. 15
B. 16
C. 17
D. 18
E. 19

Answer:

40) Choose the correct answer for the following problem. Write your answer below:

Frank and Hue had 31 comics between them. Frank had 9 more than Hue. How many comics did Hue have?

A. 15
B. 14
C. 13
D. 12
E. 11

Answer:

www.My11PlusPapers.co.uk

Verbal Reasoning - Test 13

Time allowed for this paper : 60 minutes

Instructions for Best Practice:

> Attempt all of the questions.
> Ensure that your answers are clearly marked in the answer boxes.
> Calculators and rulers must not be used.
> Equipment recommended: 2 x Pencil & 1 x Eraser.

Secondary Entrance

Marks

1) Select the word from the brackets that will complete the sentence in the most sensible way. Write your answer below:

Orange is to FRUIT as carrot is to (vegetable, orange, food)

Answer:

6) Three consecutive letters are removed from the word in CAPITALS. These letters make a word. From the options, find the missing letters to complete the sentence. Write your answer below:

Mike is renting an APMENT in the city.

A. ALL
B. ARC
C. ALL
D. AND
E. ART

Answer:

2) Find one word from each group that together makes one correctly spelt word. The letters must not be rearranged. The word from the first group must always be used first. Write your answer below:

He placed his (head, hand, shoulder) (tie, band, string) on his forehead before the tennis match.

A. Headtie   D. Headband
B. Handtie   E. Handstring
C. Shoulderstring

Answer:

7) Work out the relationship between the word and the code to solve the code and write your answer below:

A B C D E F G H I J K L M N O P Q R S T U V W X Y Z

Your teacher gives you the following code to decipher for your homework.

DOCTOR is to GRFWRU. What is the code for NURSE?

Answer:

3) Select the TWO odd words from the options given. Write your answer below:

Potato, carrot, daffodil, roses, snowdrop, jasmine.

A. Potato roses
B. Daffodil carrot
C. Potato carrot
D. Roses snowdrop
E. Carrot snowdrop

Answer:

8) Work out the relationship between the word and the code to solve the code and write your answer below:

A B C D E F G H I J K L M N O P Q R S T U V W X Y Z

Your teacher gives you the following code to decipher for your homework.

DOCTOR is to GRFWRU. What is the code for TEACHER?

Answer:

4) Choose the correct answer to complete the following functions and sums with the correct numbers and signs as appropriate. Write your answer below:

$13 \times \underline{\quad} = 45 + 7$

A. 4
B. 5
C. 6
D. 7
E. 8

Answer:

9) Using the provided code, complete the following sums writing your answer in numbers:

aa = 6, bb = 3, cc = 2, dd =15, ee = 7

Solve: aa − bb × cc =__?

Answer:

5) The words in brackets are formed from the main word. Identify the pattern to work out the missing word from the options given. Write your answer below:

Legal (leg), match (hat), minus (?)

A. SIM
B. MIN
C. SIN
D. SUN
E. SUM

Answer:

10) Write the letter that will complete the word in front of the brackets and begin the word after the brackets. The SAME letter must fit into BOTH sets of brackets. Write your answer below:

sic (_) ilt, har (_) iss

Answer:

Verbal Reasoning

75

Marks

11) Find the pair of letters that will complete the sentence in the best way. The alphabet is provided below to help you. Write your answer below:

A B C D E F G H I J K L M N O P Q R S T U V W X Y Z

DR is to ET as BS is to ___?

Answer:

12) Select the pair of words, one from each group that are **opposite in meaning** to each other from the options given below. Write your answer below:

The opposite of (throw, bat, hit) is (catch, receive, hand).

A. Throw catch
B. Bat catch
C. Hit receive
D. Hit hand
E. Throw hand

Answer:

13) Read the information provided and choose the single best answer for the question. Write your answer below:

Nikhil is facing South-West. He then turns 270°clockwise, 90° anti-clockwise and then 270° clockwise.
He then finally turns 270° anti-clockwise. What direction is he now facing?

A. North-East   D. North
B. South-West   E. West
C. North-West

Answer:

14) Read the information provided and choose the single best answer for the question. Write your answer below:
Nikhil is facing South-West. He then turns 270°clockwise, 90° anti-clockwise and then 270° clockwise.
He then finally turns 270° anti-clockwise.

What direction is directly opposite the direction he is now facing?

A. North-East   D. North
B. South-West   E. West
C. North-West

Answer:

15) A four letter word is hidden between two words in the sentence below. These two words are always next to each other, but there may be punctuation between them. Find this four letter word from one of the options. Write your answer below:

The bad replica showed the importance of getting an original.

A. showed the   D. importance of
B. replica showed E. the importance
C. bad replica

Answer:

16) A four letter word is hidden between two words in each sentence below. These **two words are always next to each other**, but there may be punctuation between them. Find this **four letter word** from one of the options. Write your answer below:

The net used by the fisherman was too small to catch anything.

A. too small   D. catch anything
B. fisherman was E. was too
C. the net

Answer:

17) Find the numbers that best complete the series. Fill in the missing blank with one of the following options and write your answer below:

84 trees, 73 leaves, 62 trees, 51 leaves, ___

A. 39 trees
B. 40 trees
C. 49 leaves
D. 42 leaves
E. 30 trees

Answer:

18) Find one word from each group that together makes one correctly spelt word. The letters must not be rearranged. The word from the first group must always be used first. Write your answer below:

Grandad used a (mouth, gum, tooth) (pull, lift, pick) to clean his teeth after dinner.

A. Gumpull   D. Toothpull
B. Mouthpick   E. Mouthlift
C. Toothpick

Answer:

19) Find the pair of letters that will continue the series. The alphabet is provided below to help you. Write your answer below:

A B C D E F G H I J K L M N O P Q R S T U V W X Y Z

BC, FG, JK, NO, RS, ___?

Answer:

20) Choose the correct answer to complete the following functions and sums with the correct numbers and signs as appropriate. Write your answer below:

$110 - 11 = 11 \times$ ___

A. 7
B. 8
C. 9
D. 10
E. 11

Answer:

Marks

21) Choose the correct answer for the following problem. Write your answer below:

When I subtract 7 from a certain number, the answer is one-seventh of 35. What is the number?

A. 15
B. 14
C. 13
D. 12
E. 11

Answer:

22) In each set of numbers, the number in the brackets is related to the two numbers either side of it. Find this relation to work out the missing number '(?)' in the third set. Choose one of the option and write your answer below:

17 (8) 9, 14 (4) 10, 8 (?) 2

A. 25
B. 12
C. 22
D. 2
E. 6

Answer:

23) Find the number that best completes the series. Fill in the missing blank with one of the following options and write your answer below:

112, 102, 93, 85, ___

A. 75
B. 78
C. 81
D. 73
E. 83

Answer:

24) The words in brackets are formed from the main word. Identify the pattern to work out the missing word from the options given. Write your answer below:

Cause (sea), battler (era), larger (?)

A. LEG
B. LAR
C. GEL
D. ARE
E. ERA

Answer:

25) Three consecutive letters are removed from the word in CAPITALS. These letters make a word. From the options, find the missing letters to complete the sentence. Write your answer below:

Donna DEDED more attention at work.

A. MEN
B. MET
C. MAT
D. MAN
E. BOY

Answer:

26) In each set of numbers, the number in the brackets is related to the two numbers either side of it. Find this relation to work out the missing number '(?)' in the third set. Choose one of the options and write your answer below:

21 (10) 11, 24 (2) 22, 23 (?) 12

A. 9
B. 21
C. 25
D. 11
E. 2

Answer:

27) Three consecutive letters have been taken out of a word. Select which three letters have been omitted from the options. Write your answer below:

Andy took a S___ER in the morning.

A. ONE
B. HOW
C. HOT
D. OWN
E. HOP

Answer:

28) You are required to move one letter from the first word to the second word, creating two new words. Write your answer below:

PUNT POD.

Answer:

29) Using the provided code, complete the following sums writing your answer in numbers:

aa = 1, bb = 12, cc = 9, dd = 5, ee = 4

Solve: bb − cc × aa + dd = ___?

Answer:

30) Write the letter that will complete the word in front of the brackets and begin the word after the brackets. The SAME letter must fit into BOTH sets of brackets. Write your answer below:

mod (_) xit, mak (_) ach

Answer:

Marks

31) Find the pair of letters that will complete the sentence in the best way. The alphabet is provided below to help you. Write your answer below:

A B C D E F G H I J K L M N O P Q R S T U V W X Y Z

FX is to DY as JZ is to ___?

Answer:

32) Select the pair of words, one from each group that are **opposite in meaning** to each other from the options given. Write your answer below:

The opposite of (easy, right, hard) is (difficult, simple, correct).

A. Easy simple
B. Easy difficult
C. Hard correct
D. Hard difficult
E. Right correct

Answer:

33) Select the TWO odd words from the options given. Write your answer below:

Envelopes, stamps, send, post, pens

A. Stamps post
B. Pens envelopes
C. Send pens
D. Send post
E. Envelopes stamps

Answer:

34) Choose the correct answer for the following problem. Write your answer below:

Lucy has 3 times as many balloons as Anjali and half as many as Pippa who has 12 balloons.
If Lucy gave 2 of her balloons to Anjali and Pippa gave 1 to Anjali, how many would Anjali then have?

A. 4   D. 7
B. 5   E. 8
C. 6

Answer:

35) Three consecutive letters have been taken out of a word. Select which three letters have been omitted from the options. Write your answer below:

She was S____DING for the entire concert.

A. TAG
B. TIG
C. TAN
D. TAP
E. TIP

Answer:

36) You are required to **move one letter from the first word** to the second word, creating two new words. Write your answer below:

PASTE BAN.

Answer:

37) Select the two words inside the brackets that are connected in some way to the words outside the brackets. Write your answer below:

Yanto only likes certain types of animals. He likes the MONKEY CHIMPANZEE (ape, gorilla, zebra, elephant, giraffe)

Answer:

38) Select the two words inside the brackets that are connected in some way to the words outside the brackets. Write your answer below:

James only likes certain types of plants. He likes the BIRCH OAK (rose, pine, beech, beach, daffodil)

Answer:

39) Select the word from the brackets that will complete the sentence in the most sensible way. Write your answer below:

Parrot is to BIRD as frog is to (mammal, amphibian, reptile)

Answer:

40) Find the pair of letters that will continue the series. The alphabet is provided below to help you. Write your answer below:

A B C D E F G H I J K L M N O P Q R S T U V W X Y Z

11PF, 33QE, 55RD, 77SC, 99TB, ___?

Answer:

www.My11PlusPapers.co.uk

Verbal Reasoning - Test 14

Time allowed for this paper : 60 minutes

Instructions for Best Practice:

> Attempt all of the questions.
> Ensure that your answers are clearly marked in the answer boxes.
> Calculators and rulers must not be used.
> Equipment recommended: 2 x Pencil & 1 x Eraser.

Secondary Entrance

1) Choose the correct answer for the following problem. Write your answer below:

Share 15 apples between Tina and Tom so that for every ONE apple Tina gets, Tom gets TWO apples. How many less than Tom did Tina get?

A. 3
B. 4
C. 5
D. 6
E. 7

Answer:

6) Find the numbers that best complete the series. Fill in the missing blank with one of the following options and write your answer below:

241, 239, 242, 238, 243, ___

A. 237
B. 240
C. 251
D. 253
E. 234

Answer:

2) Read the information provided and choose the single best answer for the question. Write your answer below:

Nikhil is facing South-West. He then turns 270°clockwise, 90° anti-clockwise and finally 270° clockwise.
Through how many degrees anticlockwise must he turn to face his original direction?

A. 0°   D. 180°
B. 45°   E. 270°
C. 90°

Answer:

7) Choose the correct answer to complete the following functions and sums with the correct numbers and signs as appropriate. Write your answer below:

51 + ___ = 16 × 4

A. 36
B. 29
C. 17
D. 13
E. 24

Answer:

3) Read the information provided and choose the single best answer for the question. Write your answer below:

Tea costs half as much as coffee in a café. Two teas and 1 coffee cost £6. How much is coffee?

A. £1
B. £2
C. £3
D. £4
E. £5

Answer:

8) Choose the correct answer for the following problem. Write your answer below:

A number plus one-third of twelve equals eleven. What is the number?

A. 4
B. 5
C. 6
D. 7
E. 8

Answer:

4) A four letter word is hidden between two words in the sentence below. These two words are always next to each other, but there may be punctuation between them. Find this four letter word from one of the options. Write your answer below:

My llama stood proud when photographed by the tourists.

A. My llama   D. proud when
B. stood proud   E. when photographed
C. llama stood

Answer:

9) Find the pair of letters that will complete the sentence in the best way. The alphabet is provided below to help you. Write your answer below:

A B C D E F G H I J K L M N O P Q R S T U V W X Y Z

HI is to MN as QR is to ___?

Answer:

5) A four letter word is hidden between two words in the sentence below. These two words are always next to each other, but there may be punctuation between them. Find this four letter word from one of the options. Write your answer below:

Church attendance has stayed the same over the last 5 years.

A. stayed the   D. church attendance
B. over the   E. attendance has
C. same over

Answer:

10) Select the pair of words, one from each group that are opposite in meaning to each other from the options given below. Write your answer below:

The opposite of (morning, noon, dawn) is (day, midnight, week)

A. Morning midnight
B. Noon midnight
C. Dawn week
D. Noon day
E. Dawn midnight

Answer:

Verbal Reasoning

80

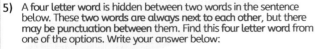

Marks

11) Select the word from the brackets that will complete the sentence in the most sensible way. Write your answer below:

Run is to FAST as walk is to (slow, stroll, path)

Answer:

12) Find one word from each group that together makes one correctly spelt word. The letters must not be rearranged. The word from the first group must always be used first. Write your answer below:

You need to come down to have dinner (some, many, same) (time, hour, week).

A. Sometime   D. Samehour
B. Sametime   E. Somehour
C. Manyweek

Answer:

13) Using the provided code, complete the following sums writing your answer in numbers:

af = 6, bf = 3, cf = 2, df =15, ef = 7

Solve: ef + df ÷ bf = ___?

Answer:

14) Using the provided code, complete the following sums writing your answer in numbers:

af = 6, bf = 3, cf = 2, df =15, ef = 7

Solve: df ÷ bf x cf = ___?

Answer:

15) Write the letter that will complete the word in front of the brackets and begin the word after the brackets. The SAME letter must fit into BOTH sets of brackets. Write your answer below:

tra (_) oat, bea (_) ate

Answer:

16) Work out the relationship between the word and the code to solve the code and write your answer below:

A B C D E F G H I J K L M N O P Q R S T U V W X Y Z

You walk into an abandoned temple and discover the following code inscribed on the wall.

DOCTOR is to GRFWRU.

What is the code for POLICE?

Answer:

17) Work out the relationship between the word and the code to solve the code and write your answer below:

A B C D E F G H I J K L M N O P Q R S T U V W X Y Z

You walk into an abandoned temple and discover the following code inscribed on the wall.

DOCTOR is to GRFWRU.

<u>Decode</u> the following: KRVSLWDO?

Answer:

18) Write the letter that will complete the word in front of the brackets and begin the word after the brackets. The SAME letter must fit into BOTH sets of brackets. Write your answer below:

lim (_) ank, sta (_) ark

Answer:

19) Select the TWO odd words from the options given. Write your answer below:

Thames, London, Egypt, Nile, Amazon

A. London Thames
B. Egypt Nile
C. Thames Nile
D. London Egypt
E. Nile Thames

Answer:

20) Choose the correct answer to complete the following functions and sums with the correct numbers and signs as appropriate. Write your answer below:

46 − ___ = 7 × 3

A. 37
B. 25
C. 22
D. 35
E. 18

Answer:

Secondary Entrance

Marks

21) The words in brackets are formed from the main word. Identify the pattern to work out the missing word from the options given. Write your answer below:

Motor (rot), needs (see), pitch (?)

A. PIT
B. CIT
C. HIT
D. TCH
E. PITH

Answer:

26) Select the TWO odd words from the options given. Write your answer below:

Turnip, cabbage, apple, beetroot, orange

A. Apple orange
B. Apple turnip
C. Cabbage beetroot
D. Orange beetroot
E. Turnip cabbage

Answer:

22) Find the numbers that best complete the series. Fill in the missing blank with one of the following options and write your answer below:

62, 28, 60, 31, 58, 34, ___

A. 54
B. 38
C. 47
D. 33
E. 56

Answer:

27) The words in brackets are formed from the main word. Identify the pattern to work out the missing word from the options given. Write your answer below:

Smudge (emu), sugar (rug), theft (?)

A. FET
B. HET
C. FTE
D. THE
E. FEH

Answer:

23) Select the two words inside the brackets that are connected in some way to the words outside the brackets. Write your answer below:

HAND LEG (bag, hat, arm, finger, shoe)

Answer:

28) Three consecutive letters are removed from the word in CAPITALS. These letters make a word. From the options, find the missing letters to complete the sentence. Write your answer below:

Bhagwat thought the pair of shoes were EXSIVE.

A. PAN
B. POT
C. PIN
D. PEN
E. PAT

Answer:

24) Select the word from the brackets that will complete the sentence in the most sensible way. Write your answer below:

Boy is to BROTHER as girl is to (mother, child, sister)

Answer:

29) Find the pair of letters that will continue the series. The alphabet is provided below to help you. Write your answer below:

A B C D E F G H I J K L M N O P Q R S T U V W X Y Z

DA, AZ, XY, UX, RW, ___?

Answer:

25) Find one word from each group that together makes one correctly spelt word. The letters must not be rearranged. The word from the first group must always be used first. Write your answer below:

The food we had at dinner was tasty and (whole, all, complete) (some, part, section).

A. Wholesome   D. Completesection
B. Allsome   E. Wholepart
C. Allpart

Answer:

30) Find the pair of letters that will complete the sentence in the best way. The alphabet is provided below to help you. Write your answer below:

A B C D E F G H I J K L M N O P Q R S T U V W X Y Z

GU is to HV as NW is to ___?

Answer:

Secondary Entrance

Marks

31) Select the pair of words, one from each group that are opposite in meaning to each other from the options given. Write your answer below:

The opposite of (carry, hold, push) is (touch, pull, hit).

A. Push touch
B. Hold hit
C. Carry pull
D. Push pull
E. Hold pull

Answer:

32) Three consecutive letters are removed from the word in CAPITALS. These letters make a word. From the options, find the missing letters to complete the sentence. Write your answer below:

Harvey only liked one BD of cornflakes.

A. RAN
B. RUN
C. CAN
D. RUT
E. CUT

Answer:

33) In each set of numbers, the number in the brackets is related to the two numbers either side of it. Find this relation to work out the missing number '(?)' in the third set. Choose one of the options and write your answer below:

13 (3) 10, 14 (3) 11, 12 (?) 6

A. 2
B. 3
C. 25
D. 6
E. 11

Answer:

34) In each set of numbers, the number in the brackets is related to the two numbers either side of it. Find this relation to work out the missing number '(?)' in the third set. Choose one of the option and write your answer below:

4 (2) 2, 7 (1) 6, 5 (?) 1

A. 15
B. 14
C. 4
D. 9
E. 12

Answer:

35) Three consecutive letters have been taken out of a word. Select which three letters have been omitted from the options. Write your answer below:

The skier was very VER____ILE when navigating the slope.

A. TAP
B. SIT
C. SAT
D. SUM
E. SIP

Answer:

36) You are required to move one letter from the first word to the second word, creating two new words. Write your answer below:

STUN SAND.

Answer:

37) Select the two words inside the brackets that are connected in some way to the words outside the brackets. Write your answer below:

PLANE TRAIN (airport, station, road, helicopter, car)

Answer:

38) Find the pair of letters that will continue the series. The alphabet is provided below to help you. Write your answer below:

A B C D E F G H I J K L M N O P Q R S T U V W X Y Z

GK, HM, IO, JQ, KS, ___?

Answer:

39) Three consecutive letters have been taken out of a word. Select which three letters have been omitted from the options. Write your answer below:

My father had to pay a lot of T____S.

A. AXE
B. ARM
C. HAM
D. EAT
E. HIT

Answer:

40) You are required to move one letter from the first word to the second word, creating two new words. Write your answer below:

SPEND ACE.

Answer:

Verbal Reasoning - Test 15

Time allowed for this paper : 60 minutes

Instructions for Best Practice:

> Attempt all of the questions.
> Ensure that your answers are clearly marked in the answer boxes.
> Calculators and rulers must not be used.
> Equipment recommended: 2 x Pencil & 1 x Eraser.

Verbal Reasoning - Test 15

Marks

1) Three consecutive letters have been taken out of a word. Select which three letters have been omitted from the options. Write your answer below:

The S___E was left in the shed.

A. PAN
B. PEN
C. PUN
D. PAD
E. BAN

Answer:

6) Select the TWO odd words from the options given. Write your answer below:

Bolivia, Paris, Berlin, Hungary, Peru

A. Paris Peru
B. Paris Berlin
C. Berlin Bolivia
D. Hungary Peru
E. Peru Bolivia

Answer:

2) You are required to move one letter from the first word to the second word, creating two new words. Write your answer below:

CHART ARM

Answer:

7) Three consecutive letters are removed from the word in CAPITALS. These letters make a word. From the options, find the missing letters to complete the sentence. Write your answer below:

Tom wrote his instructions on some PR.

A. ATE
B. ART
C. ARM
D. ARC
E. APE

Answer:

3) Select the two words inside the brackets that are connected in some way to the words outside the brackets. Write your answer below:

METRE FEET (yard, ounce, pound, gram, mile)

Answer:

8) In each set of numbers, the number in the brackets is related to the two numbers either side of it. Find this relation to work out the missing number '(?)' in the third set. Choose one of the options and write your answer below:

12 (6) 6, 13 (7) 6, 15 (?) 2

A. 5
B. 13
C. 19
D. 6
E. 2

Answer:

4) Select the word from the brackets that will complete the sentence in the most sensible way. Write your answer below:

Grass is to GREEN as tomato is to (purple, green, red)

Answer:

9) In each set of numbers, the number in the brackets is related to the two numbers either side of it. Find this relation to work out the missing number '(?)' in the third set. Choose one of the option and write your answer below:

11 (2) 9, 10 (4) 6, 6 (?) 3

A. 3
B. 22
C. 24
D. 18
E. 1

Answer:

5) Select the pair of words, one from each group that are opposite in meaning to each other from the options given. Write your answer below:

The opposite of (shop, buy, lend) is (sell, market, present).

A. Shop sell
B. Lend market
C. Buy present
D. Shop market
E. Buy sell

Answer:

10) A four letter word is hidden between two words in the sentence below. These two words are always next to each other, but there may be punctuation between them. Find this four letter word from one of the options. Write your answer below:

Have you heard about the new movie?

A. have you
B. you heard
C. heard about
D. new movie
E. the new

Answer:

Verbal Reasoning

www.My11PlusPapers.co.uk

Secondary Entrance

11) A four letter word is hidden between two words in the sentence below. These **two words are always next to each** other, but there may be punctuation between them. Find this **four letter word** from one of the options. Write your answer below:

Get a bank loan now! Interest rates have decreased over the last year.

Answer:

A. bank loan   D. the last
B. rates have   E. a bank
C. decreased over

16) Select the **TWO odd words** from the options given. Write your answer below:

England, London, Denmark, Chicago, Delhi

A. England London
B. London Chicago
C. Delhi England
D. Denmark London
E. England Denmark

Answer:

12) Find the numbers that best complete the series. Fill in the missing blank with one of the following options and write your answer below:

8, 17, 7, 16, 6, 15, ___

A. 14
B. 5
C. 11
D. 6
E. 9

Answer:

17) Choose the correct answer by completing the following functions and sums with the **correct numbers and signs** as appropriate. Write your answer below:

$252 = 240 + 6 \times$ ___

A. 5
B. 4
C. 3
D. 2
E. 1

Answer:

13) Find the pair of letters that will continue the series. The alphabet is provided below to help you. Write your answer below:

A B C D E F G H I J K L M N O P Q R S T U V W X Y Z

BG, FH, JI, NJ, RK, ___?

Answer:

18) Read the information provided and choose the single best answer for the question. Write your answer below:

Four children, Sid, Kate, Jay and Priya all had a birthday today.
In one year's time, Priya will be the age Sid is now.
Jay is half of Kate's age and is three years younger than Priya.

Priya is 11 years old.
What age is Sid now?

A. 6   D. 14
B. 8   E. 16
C. 12

Answer:

14) Find the pair of letters that will complete the sentence in the best way. The alphabet is provided below to help you. Write your answer below:

A B C D E F G H I J K L M N O P Q R S T U V W X Y Z

XA is to UW as MO is to ___?

Answer:

19) The words in brackets are formed from the main word. Identify the pattern to work out the missing word from the options given. Write your answer below:

Total (lot), topic (cop), tower (?)

A. WET
B. TOW
C. TOE
D. ROW
E. ROT

Answer:

15) Select the pair of words, one from each group that are opposite in meaning to each other from the options given below. Write your answer below:

(offer, deploy, show) (reveal, hide, keep)

A. Show keep
B. Offer reveal
C. Show hide
D. Deploy reveal
E. Offer hide

Answer:

20) Find the numbers that best complete the series. Fill in the missing blank with one of the following options and write your answer below:

56, 51, 48, 43, 40, ___

A. 35
B. 36
C. 37
D. 38
E. 49

Answer:

Verbal Reasoning

www.My11PlusPapers.co.uk

Secondary Entrance

Marks

21) Find the pair of letters that will complete the sentence in the best way. The alphabet is provided below to help you. Write your answer below:

A B C D E F G H I J K L M N O P Q R S T U V W X Y Z

BB is to EG as MM is to ___?

Answer:

26) Using the provided code, complete the following sums writing your answer in numbers:

aa = 6, bb = 3, cc = 2, dd =15, ee = 7

Solve: dd ÷ bb × aa ÷ cc = ___?

Answer:

22) Choose the correct answer by completing the following functions and sums with the correct numbers and signs as appropriate. Write your answer below:

154 − 7 = 21 × ___

A. 6
B. 7
C. 8
D. 9
E. 5

Answer:

27) Write the letter that will complete the word in front of the brackets and begin the word after the brackets. The SAME letter must fit into BOTH sets of brackets. Write your answer below:

har (_) ast, sto (_) ale

Answer:

23) Choose the correct answer for the following problem. Write your answer below:

Kim adds 9 to a third of a number and gets 15. What is half of that number?

A. 5
B. 6
C. 7
D. 8
E. 9

Answer:

28) Three consecutive letters have been taken out of a word. Select which three letters have been omitted from the options. Write your answer below:

A new movie is out S___RING some very famous actors.

A. TAR
B. TAP
C. TIP
D. BAR
E. TAN

Answer:

24) Choose the correct answer for the following problem. Write your answer below:

Chocolate bars cost 10p. Two bars and one lollipop cost 53p. How much is one lollipop?

A. 26p
B. 33p
C. 30p
D. 32p
E. 34p

Answer:

29) You are required to move one letter from the first word to the second word, creating two new words. These will then complete the sentence.

BURN BEAK.
He ate a _____ during his _____ from work.

Answer:

25) Using the provided code, complete the following sums writing your answer in numbers:

aa = 6, bb = 3, cc = 2, dd =15, ee = 7

Solve: aa ÷ bb x cc + ee = ___?

Answer:

30) Work out the relationship between the word and the code to solve the code and write your answer below:

A B C D E F G H I J K L M N O P Q R S T U V W X Y Z

DOCTOR is to GRFWRU. Decode the following: VFKRRO.

Answer:

www.My11PlusPapers.co.uk

Marks

31) Work out the relationship **between the word** and the code to solve the code and write your answer below:

A B C D E F G H I J K L M N O P Q R S T U V W X Y Z

DOCTOR is to GRFWRU. Decode the following:

VWDWLRQ

Answer:

32) Write the letter that will complete the word in front of the brackets and begin the word after the brackets. The SAME letter must fit into BOTH sets of brackets. Write your answer below:

bel (_) ast, hil (_) ist

Answer:

33) Select the two words inside the brackets that are connected in some way to the words **outside the brackets**. Write your answer below:

EYES MOUTH (foot, nose, ear, arm, leg)

Answer:

34) Select the word from the brackets that will complete the sentence in the most sensible way. Write your answer below:

Orca is to WHALE as grizzly is to (dog, bear, land)

Answer:

35) Find one word from each group that together makes one correctly spelt word. The letters must not be rearranged. The word from the first group **must always be used first.** Write your answer below:

Ali was made sure to clean the (chair, table, stool) (cloth, linen, mark) after dinner.

A. Stoolcloth
B. Chairlinen
C. Tablemark
D. Chaircloth
E. Tablecloth

Answer:

36) Read the information provided and choose the single best answer for the question. Write your answer below:

Harman spent half of his money on sweets and a quarter of his money on a magazine.
If he finished with £4 how much did he have at the start?

A. £6.50
B. £16
C. £12
D. £11.50
E. £11

Answer:

37) The words in brackets are formed from the main word. Identify the pattern to work out the missing word from the options given. Write your answer below:

Undone (end), vital (lit), water (?)

A. WET
B. WAR
C. ATE
D. RAT
E. TEA

Answer:

38) In each sentence, three consecutive letters are removed from the word in CAPITALS. These letters make a word. From the options, find the missing letters to complete the sentence. Write your answer below:

Dr Josh went to work in the HOSAL.

A. PAT
B. PIT
C. PUT
D. BIT
E. BUT

Answer:

39) Find one word from each group that together makes one correctly spelt word. The letters must not be rearranged. The word from the first group **must always be used first**. Write your answer below:

His (shoe, sock, foot) (lace, tie, cord) became untied whilst running.

A. Sockcord
B. Footlace
C. Foottie
D. Shoelace
E. Shoetie

Answer:

40) Find the pair of letters that will continue the series. The alphabet is provided below to help you. Write your answer below:

A B C D E F G H I J K L M N O P Q R S T U V W X Y Z

BY, DV, FS, HP, JM, ___?

Answer:

Answers - Tests 1-15

Answer keys for all of the tests in this book

Instructions for Usage:

> Once you have completed a test, find the answers and mark the script.
> Each question is worth 1 mark, making a total score of 40.
> Review incorrect answers using the walkthrough for guidance.
> To monitor progress, use the progress chart and error tally table.

Mark Schemes

Test 1	Test 2	Test 3	Test 4	Test 5
1) B	1) A	1) C	1) A	1) B
2) 66FT	2) CI	2) B	2) A	2) A
3) D	3) B	3) B	3) A	3) PK
4) B	4) D	4) Cricket, basketball	4) A	4) E
5) 3	5) 9	5) RAT	5) E	5) A
6) EB	6) COT BEAD	6) 1F2G	6) E	6) ILL FACE
7) King, house	7) BOAT	7) POT SAND	7) A	7) E
8) Tractor, chimney	8) 5	8) ACA	8) C	8) BEAD BREAST
9) ATE GOLD	9) K	9) 8	9) A	9) D
10) A	10) Father, sister	10) 4	10) E	10) FYOZZH
11) B	11) T	11) F	11) D	11) DESK
12) Handsome	12) Television, camera	12) Cucumber, peas	12) D	12) D
13) Weekend	13) Banana	13) SIMPLE	13) C	13) School, station
14) DKEAENG	14) C	14) Courtyard	14) B	14) Sit
15) D	15) Beach	15) HHSS	15) JJ	15) D
16) FINISH	16) CG	16) 22AP	16) E	16) 66JR
17) TALE BREAD, ABLE TREAD	17) PI	17) Ascend, descend	17) B	17) AZ
18) D	18) E	18) B	18) SOCK TRAY	18) B
19) A	19) C	19) Friend, neighbour	19) WARM	19) Cows, pigs
20) C	20) A	20) A	20) COVER	20) E
21) B	21) CATCH	21) C	21) D	21) C
22) EQWTV	22) B	22) E	22) T	22) D
23) D	23) D	23) B	23) Tub, container	23) A
24) WY	24) D	24) RMCW	24) Apple	24) A
25) A	25) C	25) D	25) N	25) B
26) Backward	26) HARE SCARE	26) C	26) Apple, orange	26) D
27) RS	27) B	27) SPAR BEAT	27) Numbers	27) B
28) C	28) D	28) D	28) GJ	28) A
29) D	29) E	29) B	29) A	29) School
30) D	30) C	30) D	30) B	30) C
31) Plate, fork	31) A	31) C	31) E	31) K
32) Coach, tram	32) B	32) A	32) SUIT REED	32) E
33) C	33) B	33) C	33) Learn	33) E
34) 10	34) ON	34) R	34) C	34) D
35) T	35) A	35) SOUR	35) WH	35) E
36) C	36) C	36) KJ	36) C	36) 0
37) S	37) D	37) D	37) C	37) 0
38) D	38) E	38) C	38) B	38) WN
39) B	39) B	39) Base	39) CG	39) A
40) C	40) B	40) C	40) C	40) C

www.My11PlusPapers.co.uk

Mark Schemes

Test 6

1) E
2) N
3) B
4) C
5) CAT SCAR
6) FK
7) CHAIR
8) 3
9) 7
10) W
11) Lake, river
12) Kitchen
13) Tulip, sunflower
14) MEAT
15) D
16) B
17) LN
18) B
19) TH
20) HH
21) DAUGHTER
22) C
23) A
24) C
25) B
26) B
27) B
28) D
29) D
30) C
31) B
32) A
33) A
34) A
35) E
36) BAN REED
37) E
38) B
39) D
40) D

Test 7

1) 1
2) 1
3) C
4) B
5) A
6) D
7) C
8) A
9) C
10) A
11) C
12) E
13) A
14) AFSPAF
15) NYJYAC
16) Parrot, hamster
17) C
18) HG
19) MB
20) A
21) A
22) A
23) A
24) B
25) OD
26) FRAIL
27) E
28) STATE FOUND
29) Ant, beetle
30) WEAK
31) D
32) E
33) A
34) A
35) DH
36) B
37) TIE MASK
38) L
39) C
40) L

Test 8

1) E
2) D
3) D
4) B
5) E
6) C
7) B
8) A
9) E
10) SG
11) FMSQC
12) ALTER
13) D
14) Milk, lemonade
15) T
16) E
17) K33Q
18) B
19) C
20) B
21) B
22) BQ
23) D
24) E
25) D
26) BUT SPAN (ACCEPT BUS PANT)
27) 6
28) Magazine, newspaper
29) Track
30) 0
31) Eat
32) B
33) 11P12Q
34) B
35) E
36) E
37) D
38) C
39) CAMP SEAR
40) D

Test 9

1) PRIEST
2) WATER
3) Light
4) A
5) A
6) D
7) A
8) B
9) B
10) D
11) C
12) D
13) D
14) D
15) C
16) A
17) C
18) JH
19) Miserable
20) D
21) 5
22) 7
23) G
24) Budgie, pigeon
25) IT
26) D
27) C
28) E
29) OQ
30) E
31) C
32) RUST PAINT
33) A
34) DF
35) D
36) E
37) D
38) BAT MOAT
39) P
40) Cheetah, panther

Test 10

1) SPX
2) RUNSX
3) D
4) JI
5) C
6) E
7) B
8) A
9) A
10) E
11) D
12) R
13) Cuboid, pyramid
14) Shape
15) B
16) EG
17) C
18) A
19) B
20) D
21) A
22) B
23) B
24) E
25) WAR DATE
26) K
27) Teacher, baker
28) DS
29) B
30) C
31) 12
32) 9
33) Light
34) HA
35) D
36) D
37) C
38) A
39) A
40) ARM DOWN

www.My11PlusPapers.co.uk

Mark Schemes

Secondary Entrance

Test 11

1) B
2) SIT PACE (ACCEPT PIT ACES)
3) RINX
4) BOOK
5) YB
6) UR
7) E
8) A
9) C
10) E
11) C
12) C
13) E
14) ZA
15) D
16) 8
17) 7
18) B
19) A
20) Biscuit, pastry
21) B
22) A
23) B
24) E
25) A
26) B
27) C
28) CZ
29) C
30) A
31) B
32) Sphere
33) B
34) B
35) A
36) C
37) MOVE SAID
38) Drive
39) E
40) Ice-cream, yoghurt

Test 12

1) E
2) FAT SPEAR
3) C
4) US
5) C
6) B
7) A
8) C
9) E
10) C
11) E
12) 8
13) 109
14) H
15) Butterfly, moth
16) FOOT
17) PP
18) E
19) B
20) C
21) E
22) A
23) E
24) M
25) Scooter, motorbike
26) ACTOR
27) GROUND
28) A
29) UF
30) D
31) AIR PEACH
32) SMELL
33) LR
34) E
35) E
36) C
37) B
38) A
39) C
40) E

Test 13

1) Vegetable
2) D
3) C
4) A
5) C
6) E
7) QXUVH
8) WHDFKHU
9) 0
10) K
11) CU
12) A
13) A
14) B
15) B
16) C
17) B
18) C
19) VW
20) C
21) D
22) E
23) B
24) E
25) D
26) D
27) B
28) PUT POND
29) 8
30) E
31) HA
32) B
33) D
34) B
35) C
36) PAST BEAN (ACCEPT PATE BANS)
37) Ape, gorilla
38) Pine, beech
39) Amphibian
40) 1111UA

Test 14

1) C
2) C
3) C
4) C
5) D
6) A
7) D
8) D
9) VW
10) B
11) SLOW
12) A
13) 12
14) 10
15) M
16) SROLFH
17) HOSPITAL
18) B
19) D
20) B
21) C
22) E
23) Arm, finger
24) SISTER
25) A
26) A
27) D
28) D
29) OV
30) OX
31) D
32) A
33) D
34) C
35) C
36) SUN STAND
37) Helicopter, car
38) LU
39) A
40) SEND PACE

Test 15

1) D
2) CART HARM
3) Yard, mile
4) RED
5) E
6) B
7) E
8) B
9) A
10) E
11) C
12) B
13) VL
14) JK
15) C
16) E
17) D
18) C
19) D
20) A
21) PR
22) B
23) E
24) B
25) 11
26) 15
27) P
28) A
29) BUN BREAK
30) SCHOOL
31) STATION
32) L
33) Nose, ear
34) BEAR
35) E
36) B
37) D
38) B
39) D
40) L J

Verbal Reasoning

92

www.My11PlusPapers.co.uk

Progress Chart

After marking each Verbal Reasoning test, find where your child's test score meets the upwards arrow of the corresponding test, and draw a cross. You can find out what estimated percentage of candidates would achieve a lower score by reading off the percentile values to the right for each test. To better spot the trend of how your child is progressing in terms of test scores and percentiles, connect successive crosses with straight lines. Underneath the chart, you can write down the scores and percentiles successively so that you can quickly look back on them later.

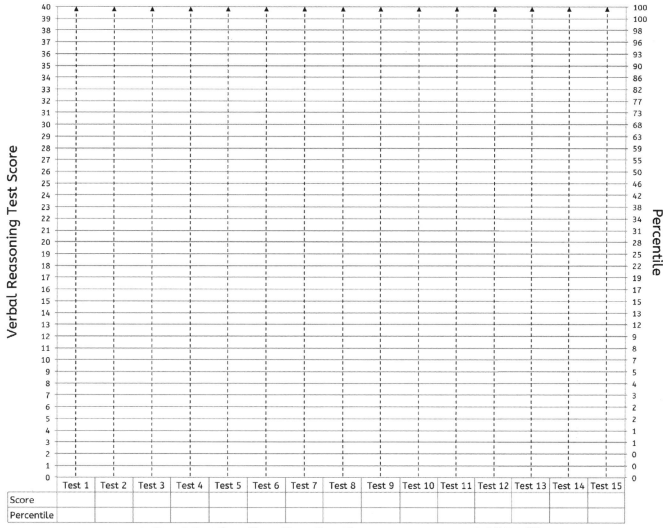

To understand and better categorise the progress charts, you can take the data and put it into the performance analysis chart on the next page. This chart allows you to develop a grading system to better study the scores that your child is getting.

We understand the value of being able to closely record and monitor your child's progress – indeed, many parents build rewards systems around them to help get their children into a steady work ethic. However, it is important that your child does not get disheartened if they do not score the mark they wanted. It is likely that as they become more familiar with the syllabus, they will achieve higher and higher marks. The purpose of this chart is for you to understand what rough level your child is at now, and to build targets around it.

On the contrary, if your child is scoring very highly, then these progress charts should provide some strong reassurance. It is important that your child keeps working through the tests to ensure that their level doesn't drop. Moreover, you may want to start thinking about scholarship programmes and raising your child's targets in accordance with these. We have intentionally included some scholarship-standard questions in every test that are of very high difficulty. It is therefore extremely uncommon that a child scores 100% in a test. We like to make sure that our papers push candidates at every level.

To build these charts, we ran trial tests around the UK and accumulated data from several students who were all due to sit independent school exams within the next 12 months. We corresponded the different scores that students were getting to the percentile that they fell within. It is important to note that while your child's scores climb, the percentile increase will follow a different pattern. Gaining 5 marks with a baseline score of 20/40 corresponds to a percentile climb of 18%, whereas with a baseline score of 35/40 the percentile climb is only 10%. It becomes harder and harder to climb those last few percentiles!

www.My11PlusPapers.co.uk

Performance Analysis Graphs and Grading

Use the graphs to analyse your child's performance. Simply take their score in any test, and read off the percentile to find out how your child did compared to others. Please note that since our tests vary in difficultly slightly, and since these graphs are estimates across all of our tests, you should take slight changes in performance lightly. It is possible for you to read off the percentiles using the progress chart on the previous page alone, but this graph makes it more clear visually how student scores are spread out. The table below the graph explains how you can grade each paper, and is colour co-ordinated with the graph.

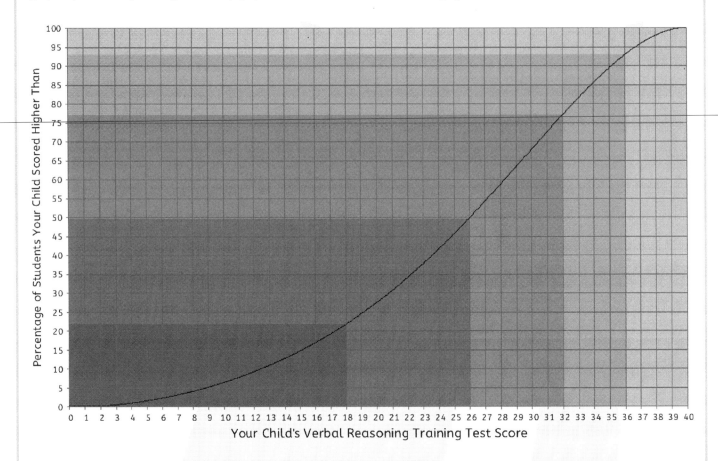

Verbal Reasoning Score	Grade
37-40	Outstanding
33-36	Excellent
27-32	Satisfactory
19-26	Coasting
0-18	Improvement Needed

Students usually need a small amount of time to adapt to different Verbal Reasoning question types, after which performance improves. Our syllabus is diverse and we have written questions from every angle to keep your child on their toes.

While sitting these papers, children should try and find methods for each individual question type that work for them. Shortcuts and tricks are easy to find, but the ones your child should use are the ones that are suited to their style of learning.

You may find this grading system useful in building up more specific reward systems for your child. Please remember that this data was collected from a large number of students who were within 12 months of sitting their Independent School 11+ examinations. We understand that some parents give their children our resources a little early, in order to get ahead of the rest of the cohort. In these contexts, the grading system may be less appropriate for them. The person who knows your child the best is you, and if these targets don't work for you, then we recommend that you change them to suit your needs.

If your child is scoring 0-18, we recommend strongly that you cover content with them before they attempt further tests. It means that there is a good chance that they are not ready to sit the tests just yet - sitting repeated tests in such a case will not build up their knowledge of first principles. At Secondary Entrance, we offer a holistic set of services, and so if you feel that your child needs help with learning the concepts, please feel free to turn to our In-Person and Skype tuition services.

If your child is scoring 37-40, their mark is outstanding. This means that they are performing extremely highly and you may want to begin thinking about scholarship training. Again, our In-Person and Skype tuition services can help you with this if you wish.

www.My11PlusPapers.co.uk

Tally Table

After marking each Verbal Reasoning test, you can refer back to the sample paper walkthrough and see which types of question your child is getting wrong. You can tally these errors here, and figure out which areas they need to work on the most.

	TEST 1	TEST 2	TEST 3	TEST 4	TEST 5	TEST 6	TEST 7	TEST 8	TEST 9	TEST 10	TEST 11	TEST 12	TEST 13	TEST 14	TEST 15	TOTAL
REMOVING SUBSET WORDS																
DECIPHERING WORDS																
REARRANGED WORDS																
INCOMPLETE WORDS																
COMBINING WORDS																
COMMON WORD ASSOCIATIONS																
ALPHABET CODES																
ALPHABET PUZZLES																
NUMBER CODES																
WORD RELATIONS																
SIMILES																
LETTER SEQUENCES																
NUMBER SEQUENCES																
OPPOSITES																
DIFFERENTIATING WORDS																
VERBAL MATHS PROBLEMS																
PRACTICAL MATHS PROBLEMS																
FUNCTIONS																
ALGEBRAIC EQUATIONS																
HIDDEN WORDS																

Some children are very ordered and logical, whereas others have their strengths in spatial problem solving or in retaining information. These differences mean that every student has a particular set of question styles which they find the most hardest.

It is only healthy for a child to work a limited number of hours in a day and, especially considering this in the run up to the exam, working smart is critical. This table helps you and your child to understand where the most scope is to gain marks quickly.

Verbal Reasoning

95

Healthy Learning Tips

11+ revision can get intense, particularly when close to the exams. It is crucial to supplement learning with a routine that consists of sufficient exercise, outdoor activity, proper diet and ample sleep, in order to stay efficient and healthy.

Can Work Become a Hobby?

How to revise without sitting at a desk

At Secondary Entrance, we truly believe in the term 'work hard play hard'. We wouldn't want your child to sit and revise abstract concepts without understanding the real life context. Sometimes it is not completely clear to a child why they may be working so hard on 11+ test papers and revising. Often it is in their benefit that they do not, to avoid unnecessary stress nearer to an exam. As an 11+ parent, being immersed within the learning process as much as your child is fundamental to their learning.

Foster a love for learning

Doing 11+ practice papers can be boring. We know because we ourselves remember all those years ago revising for our very own 11+ exams, and wanted to play outside or watch TV, not sit at a desk and do past papers. However, learning is at its best when you or your child are not aware of it, or better yet, when you are both enjoying it. By providing a learning environment that is ever-changing and engaging, learning can move outside of answering questions. Examples of this include going into the garden and counting flowers or spotting animals.

How can I Create a Structured and Varied Learning Environment?

Have something to look forward to, every time

When your child is about to start a paper, give them something to look forward to once they complete it, such as a snack, or time playing their favourite game. Having this ensures that work is not associated with unhappy thoughts, and instead is a journey, with a prize at the end of it.

Spread out the learning process in small, bite-sized chunks

A child's brain is amazing! It is able to absorb vast amount of information, more so than adults, and can learn at a very rapid rate. However, this rapid level of learning also requires regular breaks and plenty of nourishment. It is unrealistic to expect your child to work for more than an hour at a time. Create big breaks in between tests, to allow their brains lots of time to consolidate their learning.

Take learning outside of the study room!

Try going to the local park or museum! Challenge your child in new ways, such as creating maths problems using sticks or stones in the park. By making learning an engaging activity, children are more likely to retain information and are less likely to avoid working. Topics like non-verbal reasoning simply require pattern recognition, therefore spotting patterns in the environment is still learning but in a less obvious way than direct mathematics, for example. Being active within the learning process as a parent gives a child further reason to want to work. They go through this as part of a team. Leading by example is an effective means of teaching healthy learning habits.

Physical exercise is just as important as mental exercise!

It is vital that whilst you exercise your mind, you also exercise your body. Ensuring your child engages in activity every day is so important to their well-being, and also ensures that they feel fresh and energised when they do work. Whether this is swimming, running, playing in the park or football, exercise of any sort is as important as working!

Sleep!

Whilst your child works during the day, it is also important to avoid working too late at night, and that they have at least 8 hours of sleep a night. Sleep is such a valuable part of the revision process, helping the brain to filter through the information of the day, build new connections and organise it for quick retrieval at a later date. A child that is well rested will get more from a revision session than one that is sleep deprived, thus this should not be overlooked.

www.My11PlusPapers.co.uk

How can I Improve my Child's Learning Outside of School?

Going to museums

Museums are a brilliant way of bringing science, history and the arts to life. They have a lot of fun interactive exhibits to keep children entertained, but to also educate them on the fundamentals of science and art. By seeing important artefacts and demonstrations, children begin to understand the real-life applications of what they have studied.

Shopping with your child

Whilst this may simply be grocery shopping, getting them to calculate the price of the items in your basket is great for mental maths and can make any shopping trip exciting! You could also ask them to work out the price of a product after a discount, or how much you could save in your basket with 2 for 1 deals considered.

Travelling

Perhaps your child could assist you in planning a route, or finding the fastest way of getting around town. Giving them real world problems with an incentive is fun and engaging, and helps develop problem solving abilities! If in London they could plan a tube route, or if in a car they could work out how long it will take to get to your destination if you give them the distance and speed you are travelling at.

Spelling games whilst reading the newspaper

Newspapers are a great place to find fun little puzzles, such as crosswords and Sudokus. You may also be able to find a number of new words that your child has never encountered before, and be able to teach them what they mean in the process. Moreover, secondary schools that interview often like to ask about what your child may have seen in the news, and so you can keep them current on events that are happening in the world.

Playing board games such as Pictionary or Scrabble!

Scrabble is an effective means of improving a child's vocabulary in a relaxed and fun environment! It challenges them to sift through all their current vocabulary, but also to run to the dictionary to find new words! They will continually question whether certain combinations of letters make a word or not. This truly is verbal reasoning in action! Pictionary improves their visual and perceptive skills, and so may indirectly help them with maths and non-verbal reasoning. It does so in a fun way where the emphasis is on drawing and earning points.

Ultimately, Learning Should be Fun

Try to find learning resources that your child enjoys using

Whilst at Secondary Entrance we want your child to achieve the best they possibly can, it must be remembered that they are still developing socially, physically and mentally. Giving them the widest possible number of experiences and exposure to different activities is at the core of fostering life-long learning. For them to develop their own reasoning of situations is the ultimate goal of all of our papers. Our aim has been to design our resources in a way that provides long-term as well as short-term benefits to your child. We welcome any feedback about your own personal thoughts on education, as we too are also learning, and want to offer the best possible products to our clients!

How to Prepare for the 11+ Exams

At Secondary Entrance, we have all done exams. A lot of them. The majority of our staff are continually being assessed even now, and so our understanding of exams goes far beyond just being academically prepared for them.

12 months before the exam:

You and your child should familiarise yourself with the exam style for whichever exam your child will be sitting. You should try and find the appropriate syllabuses if they exist, or look at existing materials on the school's website to get a general idea of what is tested.

It is also worth keeping an eye on how your child is doing at school at this stage, and try to develop a good idea of their strengths and weaknesses. With this knowledge, you should aim to fill out any gaps in their knowledge. How can Secondary Entrance help? Within each of our 11+ practice papers, a large range of syllabus points are accounted for. In this way, you can identify the knowledge gaps early on and work smart.

Your child should attempt practice papers to get used to doing exams. This should be in a non-pressured environment, with plenty of time to read, internalise and ponder over every question. They should do no more than one paper a day, and should rotate papers to keep it mixed.

6 months before the exam:

Your child should be quite well rehearsed with the idea of taking practice papers in a relaxed environment by this stage. You may now attempt to time the papers, as per the recommendations at the front of the practice packs.

It may be that your child does not finish the paper, or that they rush near the end and miss some easy marks. These sorts of mistakes are important to make, as they will teach your child exam technique. They will learn naturally that missing out long-winded questions and revisiting them later may make sense if they are only worth one mark. Remember that getting your child into the habit of doing timed papers reduces stress closer to the exam, as they are familiar with what they will ultimately have to do.

3 months before the exam:

The number of papers your child is doing can increase up to a maximum of 2-3 per day at this point. Their timing should now be more up to speed, and you can experiment with targets to help them increase their marks further if you find that they are starting to plateau.

If your child starts to tire, or begins to adopt rout learning routines, this is often an indication that things need to be mixed up a little bit. Visit our healthy learning advice to see the variety of learning approaches that you may wish to try out.

1 month before the exam:

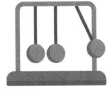

11+ exam technique is now the focus. It may help, even if only for a short period of time, to recruit a tutor who can run through technique tips with your child. A tutor can also help at this stage with topics which are proving to be a persistent problem.

The other benefit that having a tutor or otherwise constantly working with your child can have is taking care of nerves. With such little time coming up to the exam, it is normal for some panic to surface. Having a tutor can help reassure you that a professional is taking care of your child's immediate academic needs.

1 week before the exam:

At this point, most of the preparation for the 11+ should be complete, and most of your Secondary Entrance papers should be completed. Some final practice using past papers that the schools may offer on their website may help keep your child's mind freshly targeted to the specific material that they are about to encounter.

You must remember that most of the preparation at this point is complete, and that rest and leisure remain very important. Cramming hundreds of papers into this week is not an effective means of preparation, and leads to anxiety and fatigue.

The day of the exam:

All the preparation is now complete. You and your child are as prepared as they ever could be for the 11+ exam papers, and your child should have nothing to worry about. They should know what to expect for the exam, and if there is a question that they cannot do, they have adequate preparation to keep them calm and help them have as good a shot as possible.

With the help of adequate advice, tutoring and high quality preparation material, hopefully Secondary Entrance has been able to unload much of the stress for both you and your child.

Verbal Reasoning 98

www.My11PlusPapers.co.uk

Revision Timetables

A little a day goes a long way. Equally, it is important for your child not to wear themselves out by working too hard, too soon. Our revision schedules are sensible, effective and integrate healthy supplements to your child's learning.

12 Months Before the Exams

We recommend this schedule for those with a year to go before their exam - it is not too intense at all. It covers three tests in a week, and 'break-days' have a single slot to mark the previous day's paper and go over any incorrect answers.

Monday	Tuesday	Wednesday	Thursday	Friday	Saturday	Sunday
Day 1 Maths - Test 1: 60 Minutes	Day 2 Maths - Review: 25 Minutes	Day 3 English - Test 1: 70 Minutes	Day 4 English - Review: 25 Minutes	Day 5 Verbal - Test 1: 40 Minutes	Day 6 Verbal - Review: 25 Minutes	Day 7 Break: Full Day
Day 8 Non-Verbal - Test 1: 60 Minutes	Day 9 Non-Verbal - Review: 25 Minutes	Day 10 Maths - Test 2: 60 Minutes	Day 11 Maths - Review: 25 Minutes	Day 12 English - Test 2: 70 Minutes	Day 13 English - Review: 25 Minutes	Day 14 Break: Full Day
Day 15 Verbal - Test 2: 40 Minutes	Day 16 Verbal - Review: 25 Minutes	Day 17 Non-Verbal - Test 2: 60 Minutes	Day 18 Non-Verbal - Review: 25 Minutes	Day 19 Maths - Test 3: 60 Minutes	Day 20 Maths - Review: 25 Minutes	Day 21 Break: Full Day
Day 22 English - Test 3: 70 Minutes	Day 23 English - Review: 25 Minutes	Day 24 Verbal - Test 3: 40 Minutes	Day 25 Verbal - Review: 25 Minutes	Day 26 Non-Verbal - Test 3: 60 Minutes	Day 27 Non-Verbal - Review: 25 Minutes	Day 28 Break: Full Day
Day 29 Maths - Test 4: 60 Minutes	Day 30 Maths - Review: 25 Minutes	Day 31 English - Test 4: 70 Minutes	And So On...			

The 31-Day Revision Challenge

Finding a good revision routine is difficult, and your child will need to do preparation on top of training tests. This schedule slowly increases the amount of daily work done on three preparatory activities: mental maths, spelling and book reading.

Monday	Tuesday	Wednesday	Thursday	Friday	Saturday	Sunday
Day 1 Mental Maths: 10 Minutes	Day 2 Spelling Work: 10 Minutes	Day 3 Read a Book: 10 Minutes	Day 4 Break: Full Evening	Day 5 Mental Maths: 15 Minutes	Day 6 Spelling Work: 15 Minutes	Day 7 Read a Book: 15 Minutes
Day 8 Break: Full Evening	Day 9 Mental Maths: 20 Minutes	Day 10 Spelling Work: 20 Minutes	Day 11 Read a Book: 20 Minutes	Day 12 Break: Full Evening	Day 13 Mental Maths: 30 Minutes	Day 14 Spelling Work: 30 Minutes
Day 15 Read a Book: 30 Minutes	Day 16 Break: Full Evening	Day 17 Mental Maths: 35 Minutes	Day 18 Spelling Work: 35 Minutes	Day 19 Read a Book: 35 Minutes	Day 20 Break: Full Evening	Day 21 Mental Maths: 40 Minutes
Day 22 Spelling Work: 40 Minutes	Day 23 Read a Book: 40 Minutes	Day 24 Break: Full Evening	Day 25 Mental Maths: 45 Minutes	Day 26 Spelling Work: 45 Minutes	Day 27 Read a Book: 45 Minutes	Day 28 Break: Full Evening
Day 29 Mental Maths: 50 Minutes	Day 30 Spelling Work: 50 Minutes	Day 31 Read a Book: 50 Minutes				

www.My11PlusPapers.co.uk

Revision Timetables

In the Run-Up: Intense Learning

It is crucial that your child does not experience burn-out, however in the final weeks their preparation will increase. They should never sit more than two tests in a day, and our routine demonstrates the healthy way to handle the final stretch.

Time:	Monday	Tuesday	Wednesday	Thursday	Friday	Saturday	Sunday
8:00am - 9:00am	Wake up, eat breakfast, and get ready for the day!						
9:00am - 10:00am	Maths - Test 1: 60 Minutes	VR - Test 1: 40 Minutes	English - Test 2: 70 Minutes	NVR - Test 2: 60 Minutes	Maths - Test 3: 60 Minutes	VR - Test 3: 40 Minutes	NVR - Test 3: 60 Minutes
10:00am - 11:00am	Read a Book	Break: Have a snack (some fruit)		Spelling Work	Break: Watch TV or play games		Mental Maths Work
11:00am - 12:00pm	Maths Review: 25 Minutes	VR Review: 25 Minutes	English Review: 25 Minutes	NVR Review: 25 Minutes	Maths Review: 25 Minutes	VR Review: 25 Minutes	NVR Review: 25 Minutes
12:00pm - 1:00pm	Lunch Break						
1:00pm - 2:00pm	English - Test 1: 70 Minutes	NVR - Test 1: 60 Minutes	Maths - Test 2: 60 Minutes	VR - Test 2: 40 Minutes	English - Test 3: 70 Minutes	Break: Meet some friends or take part in some extracurricular activity	
2:00pm - 3:00pm	Break: Play outside and be active						
3:00pm - 4:00pm	English Review: 25 Minutes	NVR Review: 25 Minutes	Maths Review: 25 Minutes	VR Review: 25 Minutes	English Review: 25 Minutes		

Holiday Revision: Blank Timetable

It goes without saying that you know your child best, and so you may wish to create your own custom timetable for your child to work through. The working hours are limited to between 8am and 4pm, as your child is used to school hours.

Time:	Monday	Tuesday	Wednesday	Thursday	Friday	Saturday	Sunday
8:00am - 9:00am							
9:00am - 10:00am							
10:00am - 11:00am							
11:00am - 12:00pm							
12:00pm - 1:00pm							
1:00pm - 2:00pm							
2:00pm - 3:00pm							
3:00pm - 4:00pm							

Advice on Using our Timetables

As much as we want to steer you in the right direction, we at Secondary Entrance acknowledge that every child is unique, and has their own, independent learning style. In accordance with this, we strongly encourage you to modify and adjust our timetables around your child's subject needs, extra-curricular activities and their social life.

That's the end of the book. What else do we offer?

We've got a three part education system, designed to get your child into their chosen school:

1

11+ Practice Papers
240 outstanding quality tests for the 4 core subjects. We've scrutinised every question to ensure quality.

2

Tutoring Services
We offer in-person and online tutoring services. All of our tutors have attended world-leading universities.

3

11+ Practice Papers
www.Independent11Plus.co.uk
We provide learning guides and supplementary material.

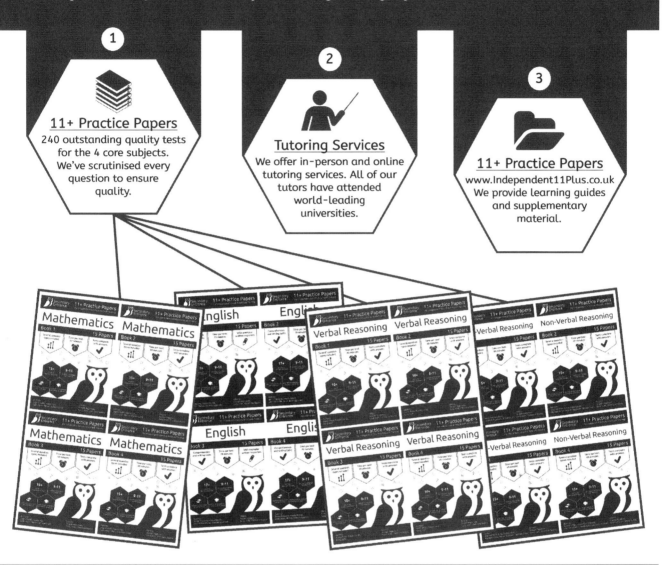

Meet our authors and editors
For verbal reasoning book 1 to book 4

Our authors have all attended Cambridge and Imperial – world-leading universities.

AUTHOR:
Aaran Patel

MBBS: Imperial
BSc: Imperial
Studying: Medicine

AUTHOR:
Russell de Sá

MBBS: Imperial
BSc: Imperial
Studying: Medicine

AUTHOR & EDITOR:
Suraj Joshi

MBBS: Imperial
BSc: Imperial
Studying: Medicine

EDITOR:
Aneesh Aggarwal

MBBS: Cambridge
BA: Cambridge
Studying: Medicine

EDITOR:
Christiana Naziris

MSc: Cambridge
BA: Cambridge
Studied: Physics

Printed in Great Britain
by Amazon

79507915R00059